1   **BREAKFAST** by Emma Sweeney (Age 6) — HIGHLY COMMENDED
2   **FROG** by Mairi Long (Age 7)
3   **FLOWER PREPARATION** by Allison Wells (Age 13)
4   **MAZURKA** by Mairi Long (Age 7) — HIGHLY COMMENDED
5   **SPARKLE** by Trudy House (Age 15)
6   **A CIRCUS CAR** by Tara Doherty (Age 6)
7   **ELIZABETH GRUEBELLEE** by Victoria Ann Watson (Age 17)
8   **HELENA** by Sarah Choonara (Age 16)
9   **A HORSE CALLED FLINT** by Josephine Stringer (Age 10) — HIGHLY COMMENDED
10   **TEDDY BOY** by Deborah Norton (Age 15)
11   **MARY AND BABY JESUS** by Victoria Alexis Fifield (Age 16) — HIGHLY COMMENDED
12   **SNOWY TREE** by Dawn Taylor (Age 6) — HIGHLY COMMENDED

£2.95

JUDY
FOR GIRLS

Printed and Published in Great Britain by D. C. THOMSON & CO., LTD.,
185 Fleet Street, London, EC4A 2HS. © D.C. THOMSON & CO., LTD., 1988.
ISBN 0-85116-414-5

The Well Of Small Wishes

IF Sue Sanders had a fault, it was that she was very shy . . . and like many shy people, she was a dreamer.

Could it be true that it's a wishing well? Everybody says it is.

Sue, do come on! We'll never get home at this rate!

Sorry, Angie. Look, do you believe that that's really a very old wishing well?

Angela Carter felt like humouring her dreamy friend.

It's supposed to be. Of course, it can't grant *big* wishes, only small ones.

I only need a small one. Hang on a minute, will you?

Listen, down there . . . I . . . I wish I had a ticket for the Happy-Heads concert this Saturday. All the tickets are sold out.

When they reached Sue's home—

Fancy someone of your age talking to wishing wells!

It's just the way I am, Angie.

Sue, a letter just arrived for you.

5

At the concert, Sue sat next to Roddy Danvers, a quiet boy she knew vaguely from school.

A ticket for the Happy-Heads concert! And no message! It's the well! Oh, if only I'd wished for someone to go with me!

Er — they're good, aren't they? Here on your own?

Yes. I . . . I was given a ticket.

Roddy treated Sue to a cool drink during the interval.

Roddy's really nice, once you get talking to him. Wonder why I've never noticed him before. Perhaps . . . perhaps he'll ask me out. He's already said he'll walk me home.

EXIT

But, later—

Er — it's been great, Sue. Er — see you.

Next morning, Sunday, Sue was back at the wishing well.

Hey, you down there! What I'd really like is a chocolate-ice with nuts! Can you manage that?

6

7

THE END

Buying a HORSE

"COME on," said Uncle John one Sunday. "We're off to buy you a horse."

Having spent the last eight and a half years growing out of my first pony, a Shetland, I couldn't believe my ears. Although I knew how to ride, I didn't quite realise what had to be known about buying a suitable horse for a twelve-year-old.

We stopped at a not-so-good riding stables that had advertised several horses for sale.

"Do you suppose they'll have anything really good here, Uncle?" I asked.

A tall man with a pleasant American accent, Uncle John smiled down at me.

"Look for a leg at each corner, a head and a tail, a straight, shortish back, good sloping shoulders, well-proportioned rump and a large bright eye — and perhaps we'll buy it," he said.

I looked carefully at each of the six ponies. The first one wouldn't see nineteen again and had high, misshapen withers — probably from an accident. The next one did his best to bite both of us. Two more were not much bigger than my Shetland, and the final two were so busy kicking at each other in the grubby little paddock that Uncle John and I piled back into the car and drove off — rather thankfully.

A second pony of around thirteen hands should be, above all, kind and sensible in and out of the stable, easy to catch, quiet to shoe, and definitely reliable in traffic. Nothing under five years old, either. After that age, they're just becoming sensible. As it has to live out, we didn't want a small thoroughbred, either, for one hard winter would give it all the ills under the sun. Something native — probably Welsh or Exmoor crossed with a bit of class such as Arab — would do very nicely. Rugged in winter, it wouldn't feel the cold too badly and a field shelter would be sufficient — plus good hay and a proper winter diet, of course.

Even so, we called at two more riding establishments before ending up in a dealer's yard a mere stone's throw away from a well-known abattoir. Here we saw a fourteen hands black gelding, who pulled like a train.

"Much too strong for a girl of twelve. In fact, hardly safe for a child at all," Uncle said.

The dealer merely grunted and led out a bay mare with a fine Arab head and neat Welsh legs. She eyed me in a calm, friendly fashion from large, interested eyes, then blew hot breath down my neck gently when I bent to pick up her front hoof because Uncle insisted that I ran my hand firmly down each leg, lifting each foot, making sure her tendons were lying flat to the bone and not thickened or strained.

There is no such thing as a perfect pony or horse. (Or a perfect person, for that matter!) This little beauty, slightly over thirteen hands, quiet in all respects, had hardly any withers — a fairly common fault.

Uncle hardly gave me time to say I rather liked her before he was asking the dealer to supply a snaffle bridle and a saddle with a crupper strap, the lot to be delivered with the mare next day.

I skipped with joy back to the car.

"Buying a horse," Uncle said, "you must not knowingly overlook anything. We now have Lady, a bridle, saddle — and, I think — quite a bargain for under four hundred pounds."

Not only did she have a leg at each corner, she could jump, too, and sailed round gymkhana courses happily showing off, sometimes bringing home some pretty rosettes and a few pounds in prize money.

I've outgrown her now. But I have her two-year-old son — called John, after my uncle. We're going to begin breaking him in slowly and carefully next summer.

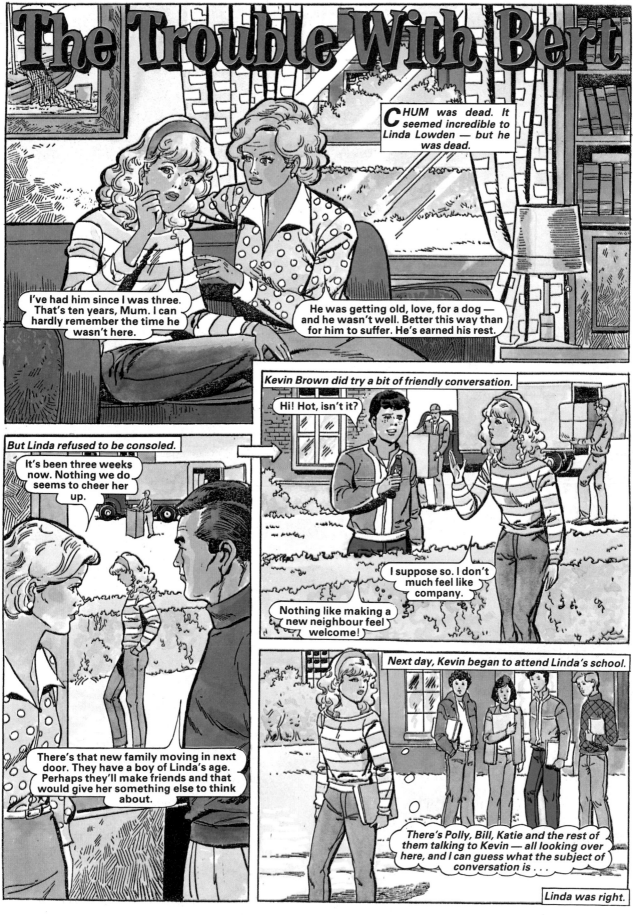

The Trouble With Bert

CHUM was dead. It seemed incredible to Linda Lowden — but he was dead.

I've had him since I was three. That's ten years, Mum. I can hardly remember the time he wasn't here.

He was getting old, love, for a dog — and he wasn't well. Better this way than for him to suffer. He's earned his rest.

But Linda refused to be consoled.

It's been three weeks now. Nothing we do seems to cheer her up.

There's that new family moving in next door. They have a boy of Linda's age. Perhaps they'll make friends and that would give her something else to think about.

Kevin Brown did try a bit of friendly conversation.

Hi! Hot, isn't it?

I suppose so. I don't much feel like company.

Nothing like making a new neighbour feel welcome!

Next day, Kevin began to attend Linda's school.

There's Polly, Bill, Katie and the rest of them talking to Kevin — all looking over here, and I can guess what the subject of conversation is . . .

Linda was right.

NOVELTY MONEYBOXES — Pop coins in the slot under their pinnies — and they'll gain pounds!

Material required:—
Empty plastic washing-up liquid bottle, approximately 20 cms. (8″) deep; one light-coloured stocking, or leg of tights; wool for hair; small patterned material for frock; circle of thin material for hat, approximately 16 cms. (6¼″) in diameter. (Draw round tea plate for this.) Narrow lace for edging neck, sleeves of frock and pinafore; small amount of suitable material for apron; ribbon for apron strings.

To Make:—
Ask an adult to do the cutting. Cut tag off top of bottle. Trace outline of face onto thin card — see *actual size* shown below. Cut out. Mark eyes in black felt pen, mouth in red. Stick round neck of bottle. Pad back of head with cotton-wool to give shape. Now, push the body inside the stocking. Mark where coin slot should go. (Under waist.) Cut slot. Draw up stocking tightly to bottle neck. Wind thread round neck, or gather, keeping fullness at back and stretching stocking flat over face. Twist stocking round top of head. Secure with stitching. Pull down stocking again to base. Tie round neck — still keeping face flat. Again mark eyes and mouth, which should still show on card. Stick, or sew, wool round head for hair.

To Dress:—
Cut oblong of material approximately 20 cms. x 33 cms. (8″ x 13″). Seam 20 cms. sides together, leaving gap for coin slot. Fold over top edge of tube. Make running stitch. Place tube over doll — keeping seam in centre front. Gather round neck.

To make sleeves:— Cut two oblongs approximately 13 x 9 cms. (5″ x 3½″). Seam along 13 cm. side. Attach one to each side of tube

Granny Penny Savers

dress. Fold pipe cleaner in half. Cover folded end with bit of stocking to make hands. Push in sleeve and gather round hand to make frilled cuff edge. Sew lace round cuffs.

To make pinny:— Cut material approximately 13 cms. (5″) square. Trim with lace. Gather top of apron. Sew apron ribbon strings at sides. Tie apron securely with bow at back. Make sure you have coin slot big enough to take coins. When moneybox is full, if you cannot get

coins out with tea-knife blade, snip a slot in base to get money out. To re-use, cut oval of strong card, cover with stocking and stitch back on to doll.

For "GRANNY PENNY-SAVER", use white or grey wool for hair and add a shawl. "MISS PENNY-SAVER" can be dressed in kitchen cloth material if you have nothing else suitable in a small pattern fabric. Both have similar hats.

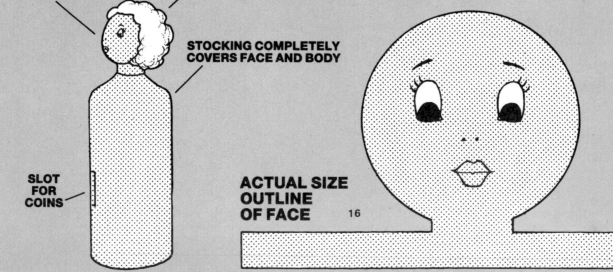

CARDBOARD FACE

COTTON WOOL

STOCKING COMPLETELY COVERS FACE AND BODY

SLOT FOR COINS

ACTUAL SIZE OUTLINE OF FACE

16

MATERIALS REQUIRED

Red material, approx. 250 mm. x 125 mm. (Felt is easiest to sew.) Narrow lace to go round edge — approx. 750 mm. long. Stuffing — cotton wool, kapok, or similar. Pins.

TO MAKE

Draw the two heart patterns onto card to make templates. (Figs 1 and 2). Lay larger heart-card on red material. Draw round with felt pen. Do the same with the smaller template. Cut out the heart shapes. Lay smaller heart card on larger heart. Draw round. This will give you a stitching line to follow.

Sew both heart shapes together except for about 40 mm. at side. (This will leave room to insert stuffing).

Turn right way out. Press, making sure the top rounded parts are really curved. Fill firmly with stuffing. Sew up the open side. Run draw thread along lace edge. Sew lace to seams frilling it as you go.

Arrange pins in shape of a kiss (x).

This is pretty — and practical!

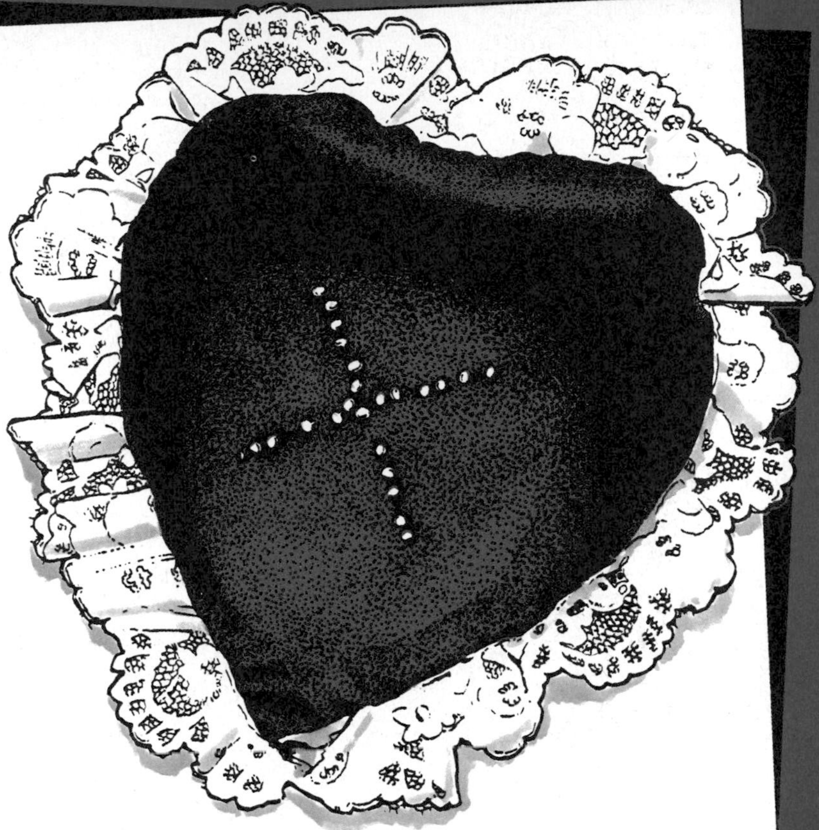

Pretty Pincushion

Make This Pretty Heart-Shaped Pincushion.

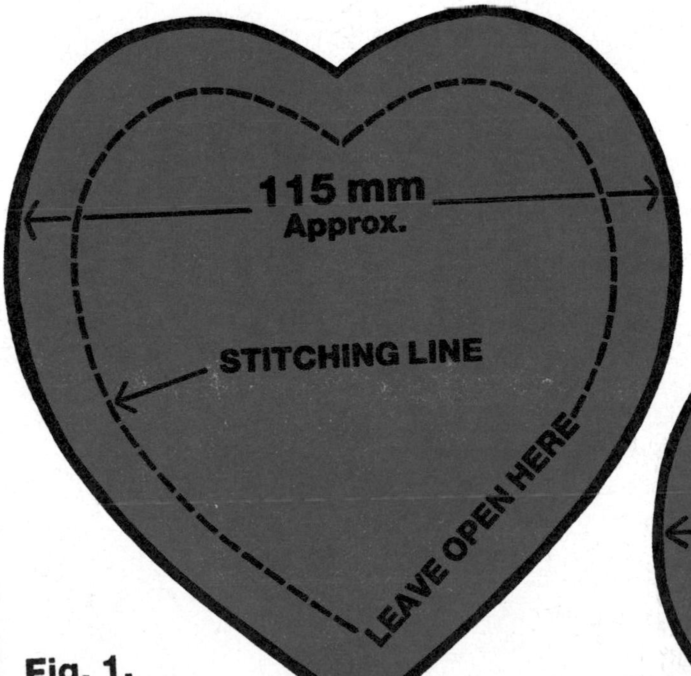

115 mm
Approx.

STITCHING LINE

LEAVE OPEN HERE

Fig. 1.

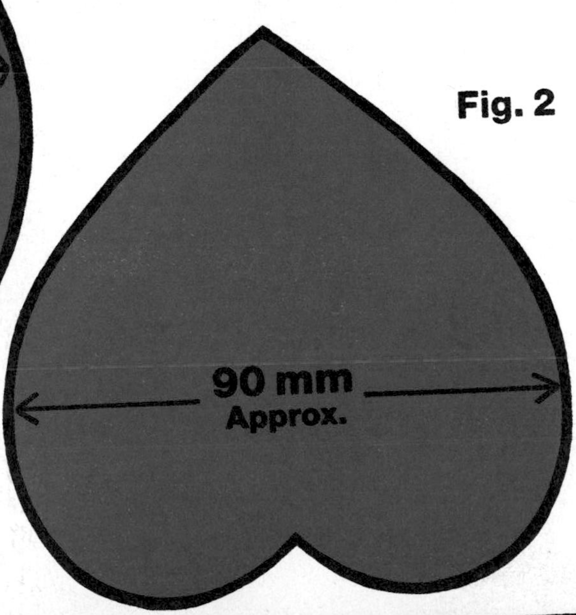

Fig. 2

90 mm
Approx.

NOT ACTUAL SIZE

PONY QUIZ

H OOF ROG ROOM ANET AILB
IT ROT ACKB RID LE GAID
AND YSTA BLEST ALL ION
ECK HAL TERW EAVI NGA
LLOP ONYHO CKSTIR RU
PUL LERE INSAD DLE

HIDDEN ABOVE ARE THE DESCRIPTIONS OF THE 24
SMALL PICS. SOME LETTERS ARE USED TWICE,
THE SPACES ARE IN THE WRONG PLACE, AND
WORDS DO NOT NECESSARILY END OR START AT
THE LINE ENDS. **HOW** MANY CAN YOU FIND?

TEST YOUR **PONY** KNOW-HOW!

18

That Holiday Spirit

GAYLE MELVIN was about to go on holiday with her parents.

Are you taking the book with you, Gayle?

I am, Mum. I just love ghost stories.

GHOSTS OF BODMIN MOOR

I do hope you won't find it too lonely, Gayle. It's a pity your sister, Deirdre, decided to stay at home.

Well, she's studying so hard for her A's, I suppose you can't blame her. I don't mind, honestly.

Hey, you two girls — are you nearly ready?

We're on our way, Steve! Midsea, here we come!

Next day at Midsea—

I wish I could join them. I just haven't the nerve to barge in, though.

Bobby Dazzler

BOBBY DAZZLER was the only girl at the Westbury Boarding School for boys, where her mother was Matron. Don Carter and Mike Norton spent their time competing for Bobby's attention — that was, when they weren't trying to put her down.

Bobby, we have to talk seriously to you. We've just got our half term reports and I'm bottom in Maths and one from the bottom in History . . .

. . . and I'm even worse. It's all because of you, Bobby.

The fact is, we spend so much time vying for your attention that we haven't time to study.

So we've worked out a way to settle it once and for all.

This is bound to be good!

I've been reading this book — and it's great. And Mike and I have decided to do what Sir Frisbian did in similar circumstances, and have a joust.

And, whoever loses steps down. It'll be easier for you, too. You won't have to keep choosing between us.

Apart from anything else, people just don't joust now. Start that and you'll be up before the Head before you know it.

It's not going to be that sort of joust, Bobby. We're going to have something more fitted to this day and age.

SIR FRISBIAN KNIGHT OF VALOUR

You're not going to box, are you?

Nothing like that. One of us could get hurt.

No, Bobby — it's conkers.

Conkers?

We're in training, as of this morning. The joust — I mean, match — will take place on Saturday.

25

27

CINDERELLA JONES

CINDY JONES' widower father had married again and taken Cindy to live in Brightsea. Cindy's new stepmother kept the Happyholme Guest House and made it plain Cindy would have to work hard for her keep while her stepsisters, Isobelle and Sarah, did nothing.

The thing I like most about Christmas, Dad, is all the surprises! I can hardly wait!

Yes, Cindy, it's such a happy time. Peace and goodwill to all.

Eeeeek!

Stepmother, what is it?

What's wrong, Agnes?

It's the electricity bill! It's enormous! So is the gas bill, and the rates demand! If things don't alter, I'll be ruined!

Come on, Stepmother. Forget about the bills for now — it's Christmas.

Christmas? More expense? You can forget it! As far as Happyholme is concerned, Christmas has been abolished!

Surely you don't mean that, Stepmother? I told the old folk we'd be having a party — with turkey and Christmas pudding and crackers and fancy hats.

Then you'd better untell them! There'll be no Christmas festivities in this house! From this moment, I am launching an economy drive!

Later —

I do love Christmas, Cindy. We were so looking forward to our party.

Don't worry, folks. I'm sure my stepmother will relent. Even she couldn't bring herself to abolish Christmas.

But, on Christmas Eve —

Cindy, it's freezing in here! The central heating's been turned off!

I know. Stepmother says it can only be switched on for one hour per day, and this is all the coal she's allowed you for the fire.

29

The CHANGING PICTURE

TINA THOMSON was cross with herself. It was the first day of her holidays and she had spent all her pocket-money on a painting of a local beauty spot.

I can't understand why you did it, Tina. It's not even a very good painting.

Well, I'm not shelling out any more pocket-money, my girl. You'll just have to manage as best you can.

I just felt, when I looked into that old junk shop, that I had to have it. Now, I hate the sight of it.

Next morning, on the way to the beach, Tina threw away the painting.

Oddly, it looked a bit different this morning — but I still don't want it.

They took a different route from the previous day, and —

Look, Tina! that's the hill in your painting — and the forest! See?

I was silly to buy that picture, Milly.

33

Somehow, Tina couldn't get into a holiday mood.

If I'd saved my money, I could have bought some souvenirs. And there's a fair coming, they say. Oh, why was I such a fool?

Tina couldn't resist picking up the painting.

All I want is to have a closer look at it. Probably the whole thing's just my imagination.

By next morning, the painting had changed still more.

The girl's farther down the hill — and she's carrying something in her shawl. It's much later, too — the moon's rising. And — and — I should be scared, yet I'm not.

The painting was still there as they returned from the beach. Glancing at it, Tina felt her scalp prickle.

It — it's changed! That girl coming down the hill wasn't there before!

I'll keep it locked away, and look at it every day just to see what happens. Another thing I'll do is find out who painted it.

Tina found out that the painter was a local artist. So that afternoon —

You were the one who bought that painting, were you? It wasn't one of my best. What attracted you to it?

I don't really know. I was hoping you'd be able to tell me!

I can't tell you much, except — well, when I was painting it, I felt . . . uncomfortable. I was glad to get it finished and out of the house. To tell you the truth, I don't want anything more to do with it.

Next day, Tina went to the public library.

LOCAL HISTORY

Somehow I've a feeling I might find something about that girl in here in a book of local history.

"Nell Red-Kirtle. A gypsy who profaned the local church in 1656 and was hounded to death because of it." Well, Nell — what are you after now?

NELL RED-KIRTLE

NELL RED-KIRTLE

The next evening, the girl in the painting was kneeling at the foot of a great oak tree.

I've seen that oak for real! It's even bigger now. She looks so furtive, looking over her shoulder. What is she doing? Or — or can I guess?

Tina, supper's ready, and Mum says . . . Oh! Isn't that your old painting? I thought you were going to get rid of it.

The Budgerigar

Budgerigars make charming pets and soon settle down as part of the family. They are easy to look after, require very little attention, and cost no more than a few pence weekly to feed. They are hardy little birds, generally remaining healthy and active throughout their long lives.

BUYING YOUR BUDGIE

A little extra care taken at this stage will be rewarded with years of friendly companionship. Seek your future pet from a reliable source — a breeder, a good pet shop, store, or garden centre. This way, you are more likely to get a well-bred, healthy bird — possibly with a guarantee. If you want your budgie to talk, you should choose a young cock or hen six to nine weeks old. Look for a quiet bird with a bright eye and all its feathers intact. Make sure the plumage lies tight to its body and that the vent is unsoiled. The colour is unimportant, except for your own preference or if you want to breed from it. Pet budgerigars, properly cared for, live an average of seven years. Claims have been made for individual budgies who have lived more than 20 years.

DID YOU KNOW?

The budgie originally came from Australia. Large flocks of wild, light-green budgies lived in the interior grasslands. The Aborigines called them "betchery-gah", meaning good to eat.

HOUSING

When you let your budgie out of its cage, do not forget to close the windows and doors, protect an open fireplace, cover up any house plants, draw curtains across any clear glass to prevent accidents — and put the cat out. If, in the early stages of its unfamiliar freedom, you experience difficulty in getting the bird back into its cage, the following method can be used as a last resort. Darken the room — drawing the curtains if need be — and seek the budgie out with a torch. Either use a hat, or something similar, to

DID YOU KNOW?

There are many famous budgie fanciers, including strongman Geoff Capes, the Queen Mother, Paul McCartney and ex-Defence Minister Michael Heseltine.

capture the bird, then envelop its wings close to the body with one hand, while keeping the thumb and forefinger each side of the head under the cheek bones. Holding the bird so, you can now pop it back into its cage. Later, your pet will return voluntarily, sometimes when commanded to do so.

Your budgie will be happier in a roomy and well-sited cage not cluttered with too many toys. The best position for the cage is opposite a window, away from a door and not higher than about four feet off the floor. Once the cage is in position, it is better for the bird if it is not moved. You can keep two budgies in an ordinary pet cage, providing they are occasionally allowed out to fly around the room, though it would be best if you had the largest practical cage.

A budgie prefers a cool, well-ventilated place. Do try to avoid draughts and direct sunlight. Have a secure box available to keep your bird in while you are cleaning out its cage. The cage, feeding pots, perches, and toys should be cleaned in a weak solution of disinfectant, such as Domestos, once a week. Rinse and dry off the items before reassembly and renew the sandsheet or loose sand floor covering. The cage can be lightly covered during the evening, or at night, to ensure that your pet is undisturbed after it has roosted.

FEEDING

The basic food is a mixture of canary seed and millet. "Trill" contains grains with essential iodine to guard against thyroid disturbances — a common complaint among budgies fed on unsupplemented seed. Minerals and vitamins are also included.

Keep the seed pots regularly filled and, once daily, blow off the accumulated husks. Never attempt to vary the amount of seed provided without expert advice. SEED, CUTTLEBONE, BUDGERIGAR GRIT AND FRESH DRINKING WATER SHOULD ALWAYS BE AVAILABLE TO YOUR PET. THESE ITEMS ARE VITAL.

Most budgies appreciate occasional titbits, such as millet spray, carrot, spinach, lettuce, chickweed, seeding grasses and apple. Green food should be well-washed, drained and fed sparingly in the morning, two or three times a week. Feed small quantities and remove the remains at the end of the same day.

DID YOU KNOW?

Breeding for different colours quickly became a craze. By 1880, the first yellow bird had been bred and, in 1910, a sensation was created at the Crystal Palace exhibition when the first blue budgerigar was exhibited.

TRAINING

The first step is to gain the bird's confidence. Allow a couple of days for settling down, then approach the cage quietly, repeating "pretty boy" or some similar two-word phrase. When your approach is accepted without apparent fear, you can start the finger training. Extend the index finger alongside a perch, raising it under the bird's breast until it hops on. Move your hand slowly around the cage, transferring your pet from perch to perch, whispering encouraging noises. In a day or two, you will be able to withdraw your hand from the cage with the bird perched on a finger. Try stroking down the beak with the index finger of the other hand. It is all good, confidence-winning training. Continue repeating the two-word phrase as often as possible and soon your patience will be rewarded. Your pet will have said its first words. Add another phrase, repeat this until perfect, and so on, thus building up a large vocabulary of which you and your budgie will be proud.

A baby budgie can, with patience, be taught to repeat its first words in about six weeks. Any bird that has not talked during the first nine months of its life is unlikely to do so — although this may not be impossible.

HEALTH

Although budgies look exotic, they are in reality very hardy little birds. New owners will soon discover that every budgie has a personality of its own, just like people. Most are active and extrovert, but a shy bird will need a little more patience to win its confidence.

A healthy budgie will be bright of eye, alert and smooth-feathered. The first sign that a budgie is ill may be seen by a fluffing-up of the feathers, dull and partly-closed eyes. The bird may sleep longer than usual, with its head tucked under its wing, or huddled-up in a corner of the cage. Only a veterinary surgeon can accurately diagnose the problem and you should seek his advice without delay.

Questions about your pet's health should be discussed with your local veterinary surgeon.
If you need further information about the care or nutrition of your budgerigar, please write enclosing a stamped self-addressed envelope to:

**PEDIGREE PETFOODS
EDUCATION CENTRE,
NATIONAL OFFICE,
WALTHAM-ON-THE-WOLDS,
MELTON MOWBRAY,
LEICESTERSHIRE LE14 4RS.**

EYE
Facing the side, giving wider vision. Young chicks have a white rim.

CERE
Blue for a male. Brown for a female.

MASK
Large round spots.

BEAK
Shaped to remove husks from seed when feeding.

TAIL
Two long, straight feathers.

FEET
Two pairs of toes on each foot, used for climbing and gripping the perch.

WINGS
Strong flight feathers.

KEEPING COLDWATER FISH

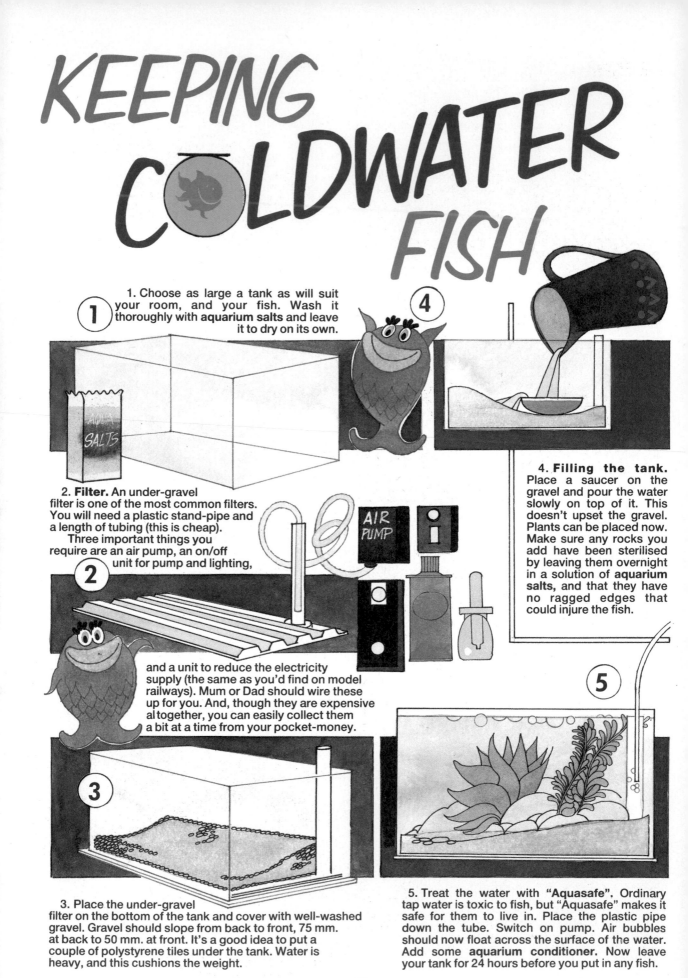

1. Choose as large a tank as will suit your room, and your fish. Wash it thoroughly with **aquarium salts** and leave it to dry on its own.

2. Filter. An under-gravel filter is one of the most common filters. You will need a plastic stand-pipe and a length of tubing (this is cheap).
   Three important things you require are an air pump, an on/off unit for pump and lighting, and a unit to reduce the electricity supply (the same as you'd find on model railways). Mum or Dad should wire these up for you. And, though they are expensive altogether, you can easily collect them a bit at a time from your pocket-money.

3. Place the under-gravel filter on the bottom of the tank and cover with well-washed gravel. Gravel should slope from back to front, 75 mm. at back to 50 mm. at front. It's a good idea to put a couple of polystyrene tiles under the tank. Water is heavy, and this cushions the weight.

4. Filling the tank. Place a saucer on the gravel and pour the water slowly on top of it. This doesn't upset the gravel. Plants can be placed now. Make sure any rocks you add have been sterilised by leaving them overnight in a solution of **aquarium salts,** and that they have no ragged edges that could injure the fish.

5. Treat the water with **"Aquasafe".** Ordinary tap water is toxic to fish, but "Aquasafe" makes it safe for them to live in. Place the plastic pipe down the tube. Switch on pump. Air bubbles should now float across the surface of the water. Add some **aquarium conditioner.** Now leave your tank for 24 hours before you put in any fish.

Choosing your fish. There are lots of cold water fish to choose from. There are Fantails (large fish), Moors (black fish), Red Orandas (small red fish), Shubunkins (mottled fish), and many more. Don't overcrowd your tank. If given lots of room, your fish will grow. Take advice, and make sure you choose healthy fish.

Feeding. Don't overfeed your fish. A pinch of mixed flake food twice a day is enough. Fish should always be rooting for food.

With the addition of a neon tube fixed securely above the tank in a cover or a low shelf, your plants and fish should thrive.

A JUDY

PONY CARE FEATURE

IF you look after your pony yourself, check the field regularly for loose or broken fence posts and slack or rusted wire. Ideally, barbed wire should not be used to fence fields for horses, but, if you rent the field and it is so fenced, make sure the wire is kept taut between the posts. Don't forget to inspect the ground for broken glass, tin cans etc.

POISON IVY

HEMLOCK

COWBANE

DEADLY NIGHTSHADE

RHODODENDRON

IVY (HEDERA)

BOX

LUPIN

FOXGLOVE

MEADOW SAFFRON

BRACKEN

LAUREL

ACONITE

LABURNUM

YEW

RAGWORT

Look carefully at the pasture and hedgerows in case of poisonous plants. The most common ones are shown here. The young, green shoots of bracken are certain death to foals and young stock.

Field and Stable

Always check the water trough and clean out regularly. In winter, break any ice twice a day so that the pony can drink. Inspect the field gate. Broken hinges or woodwork can mean an escaped pony. Also, use two padlocks and two chains ,one on each end of the gate ,for safety. Keep the locks regularly oiled. If the field has a thick hedge, check for gaps and get them properly attended to.

Last, but not least, examine the stable or field shelter. Look for sharp pieces of wood, protruding nails, broken or rusty bolts, hinges, and stable fittings. All tie - rings should be in good order and firmly fixed. Any windows should be protected with wire mesh and should open outwards, away from the pony.

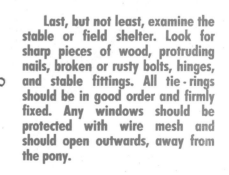

At least once a year, have stable lights and wiring checked by a qualified electrician.

46

49

Then Bellman's Close would be ideal. It's just outside Blanchester, opposite the golf links. Would you like to take the key?

I haven't time today. But I'll look through all these as soon as I can and let you know.

I'll give you my card. By the way, who was the lady who was in here when I arrived?

Mrs Kenwood, you mean?

Kenwood! Of course!

Grant Forster — the big TV producer! Gosh, Mr May will be pleased that he's chosen to consult our firm!

Later—

Mrs Kenwood has dropped her Post Office Savings Book, Hilary.

I'll take it round on my way home.

Mrs Kenwood invited Hilary in.

Oh, thank you! I must have pulled it out with my rent book. I'll show you round the house.

It's dreary and reeking of damp!

The house was in a bad way.

I know it's awful, but it's better than moving into Beckwith Lodge, which is what the welfare people want me to do.

Beckwith Lodge? The Old People's Home? But you're still very active! It's not your fault that this house is in a bad state of repair!

Nor the landlord's fault, really. The houses are old, the rents very low, and repairs cost a lot. But now you can understand why I want to find a flat. I can still work, and I sometimes get little cleaning and cooking jobs.

This is my little gallery of old friends. Ah, those were the days! We had great fun. That's John Barnett, when he played in "Twelfth Night" at the old Queen's Theatre. *Sir* John Barnett, he is now, but I'll bet he'd still make short work of my beef casserole given the chance! Next to him is Estella Roy. She's just had a West End hit.

Mrs Kenwood, how do you come to know all these famous stage people?

I was a theatrical mum. I kept a boarding house and all the stage folk used to come to me when they were playing at the Queen's Theatre. A lot of them have gone right to the top now. See that one? Know who he is?

That's Grant Forster as he was twenty-five years ago. My word, he loved my cooking! He gave up acting and went in for producing films.

I must do something to help her.

Hilary was sad when she left.

Poor Mrs Kenwood! She spent all her savings trying to find a cure for her late husband's illness and now she's come to this!

A week later, Mr Forster decided to look at Bellman's Close.

I like it very much, but it would be too much for a daily woman to cope with. My housekeepr still can't be persuaded to move to Blanchester.

Have you tried to get anyone in her place?

I like plain English food, properly cooked and served — and that's something I only get from Mrs Harvey, my present housekeepr.

Hilary knew that the producer was staying overnight in Blanchester at a hotel.

I — er — my mother would be pleased if you would have dinner with us this evening. I can promise you a good meal of traditional English food.

How kind of you!

This is going to take a lot of planning! I hope Mum agrees! And I'll need someone to dress up as a maid!

So, that evening —

I haven't tasted food like this for many years, Mrs Johnson.

Traditional apple pie followed, topped with a light, creamy cheese.

Ah! That's how I like apple pie! I suspect you of delving into my past!

We have, Mr Forster — and now we have a confession to make. The maid isn't ours and Mum wasn't the cook. I'll call the real cook.

Why! Mum Kenwood! It's great to see you again!

It's nice to see you, too.

It's going to work! Mr Forster will accept Mrs Kenwood's offer to come and keep house for him like a shot. What's more, he'll buy Bellman's Close. How do I rate as a homefinder now, eh, Mum?

Mum, Dad and I will see to the coffee and leave you to chat.

THE END

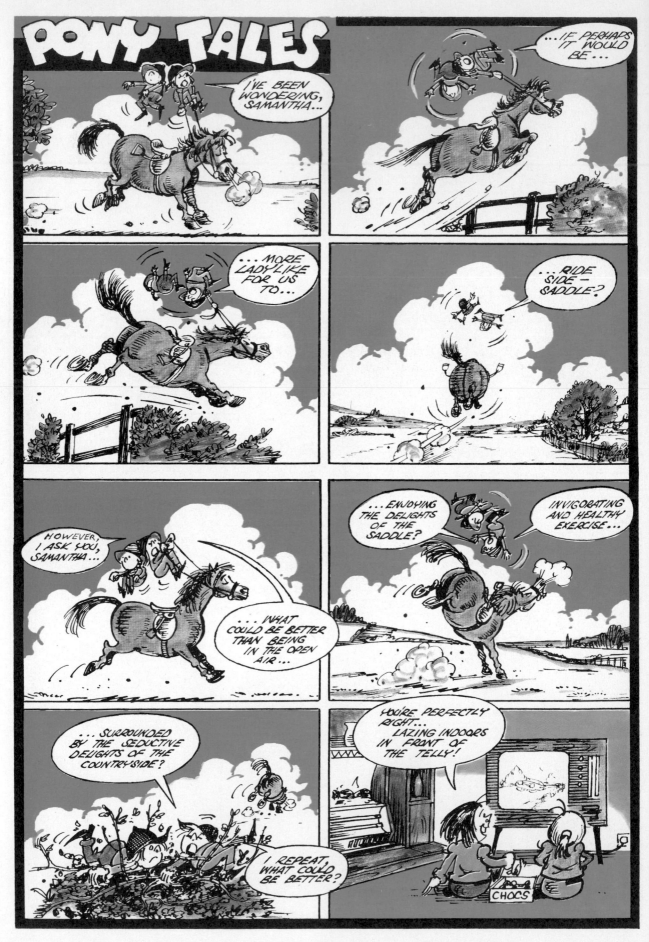

54

55

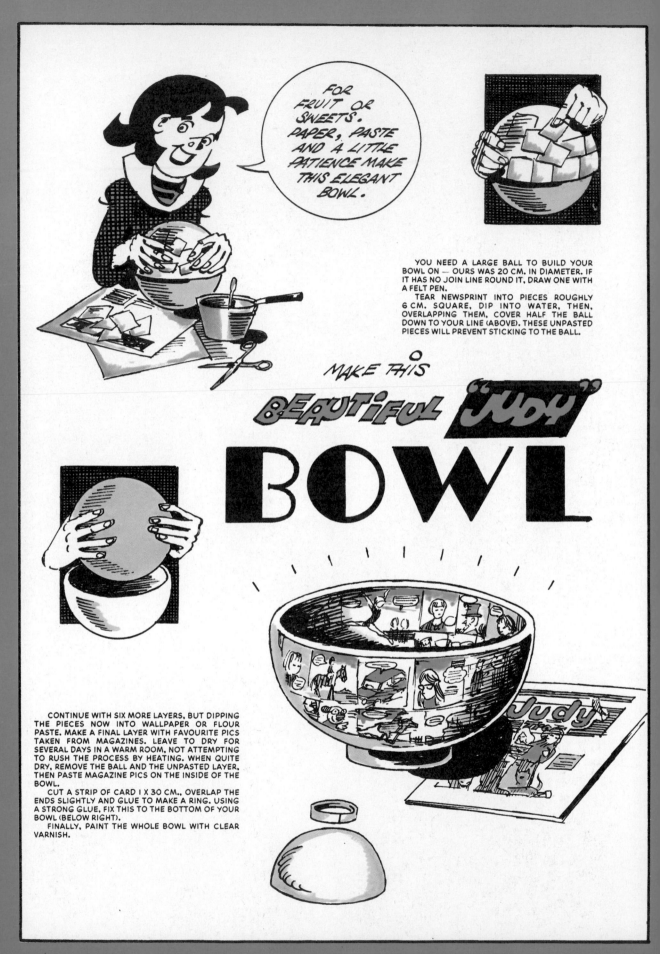

FOR FRUIT OR SWEETS. PAPER, PASTE AND A LITTLE PATIENCE MAKE THIS ELEGANT BOWL.

YOU NEED A LARGE BALL TO BUILD YOUR BOWL ON — OURS WAS 20 CM. IN DIAMETER. IF IT HAS NO JOIN LINE ROUND IT, DRAW ONE WITH A FELT PEN.

TEAR NEWSPRINT INTO PIECES ROUGHLY 6 CM. SQUARE, DIP INTO WATER, THEN, OVERLAPPING THEM, COVER HALF THE BALL DOWN TO YOUR LINE (ABOVE). THESE UNPASTED PIECES WILL PREVENT STICKING TO THE BALL.

MAKE THIS

BEAUTIFUL "JUDY" BOWL

CONTINUE WITH SIX MORE LAYERS, BUT DIPPING THE PIECES NOW INTO WALLPAPER OR FLOUR PASTE. MAKE A FINAL LAYER WITH FAVOURITE PICS TAKEN FROM MAGAZINES. LEAVE TO DRY FOR SEVERAL DAYS IN A WARM ROOM, NOT ATTEMPTING TO RUSH THE PROCESS BY HEATING. WHEN QUITE DRY, REMOVE THE BALL AND THE UNPASTED LAYER, THEN PASTE MAGAZINE PICS ON THE INSIDE OF THE BOWL.

CUT A STRIP OF CARD 1 X 30 CM., OVERLAP THE ENDS SLIGHTLY AND GLUE TO MAKE A RING. USING A STRONG GLUE, FIX THIS TO THE BOTTOM OF YOUR BOWL (BELOW RIGHT).

FINALLY, PAINT THE WHOLE BOWL WITH CLEAR VARNISH.

58

STRING BAG

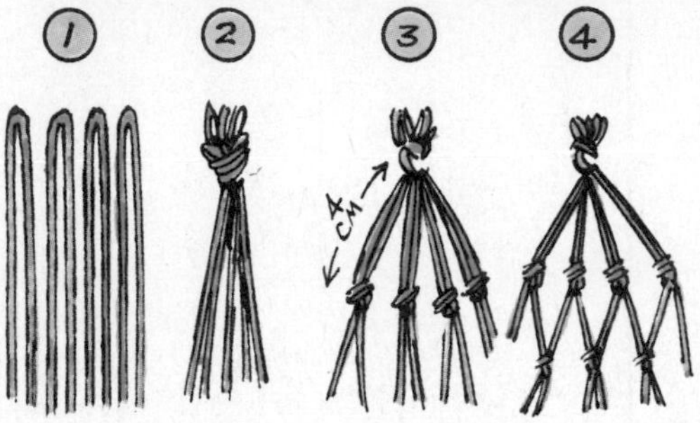

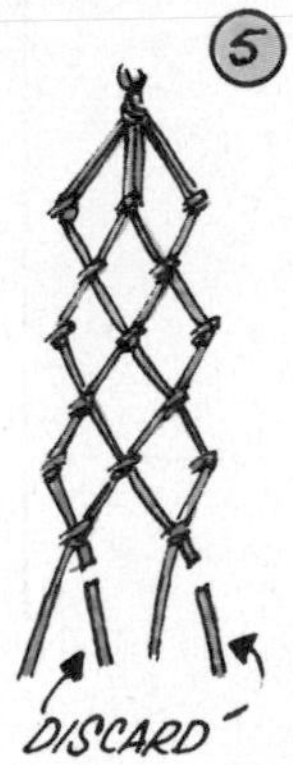

IT'S **ELEGANT**, IT COSTS VERY LITTLE, IT'S **FUN** TO MAKE, AND YOU CAN COMPLETE IT IN ABOUT THIRTY **MINUTES!**

① ② ③ ④

⑤

START WITH FOUR 125 CM. LENGTHS OF STRING. FOLD THEM ALL IN HALF (1) AND TIE AS SHOWN (2).

TAKE TWO OF THE STRANDS AND MAKE A SIMPLE OVER-AND-THROUGH KNOT 4 CM. FROM THE FIRST KNOT. DO THE SAME WITH THE THREE OTHER PAIRS (3).

NOW PULL ALTERNATE STRINGS TOGETHER AND KNOT AGAIN AT 4 CM. INTERVALS (4), CONTINUING LIKE THIS UNTIL YOU HAVE SIX LEVELS (5). TRIM OFF ONE OF EACH PAIR, AS SHOWN.

NOTE THAT WE SHOW HERE ONLY PART OF THE BAG CIRCUMFERENCE — THE OTHER PART IS BEHIND, AS IT'S A TUBE.

DRAW THE BOTTOM STRINGS TOGETHER AND TIE A LARGE SIMPLE KNOT AT THE END, THIS BEING THE HANDLE — THAT IS, THE TOP OF YOUR BAG.

IT WILL TAKE THE SHAPE OF WHATEVER YOU PUT IN IT.

DISCARD

AND OF COURSE, IT'S **SO USEFUL!**

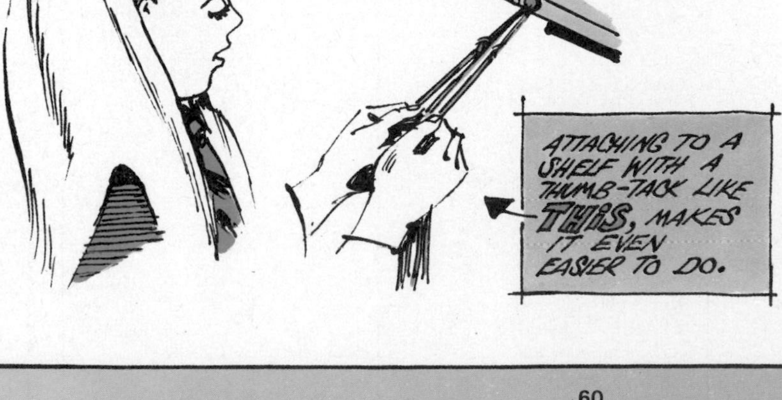

ATTACHING TO A SHELF WITH A THUMB-TACK LIKE **THIS**, MAKES IT EVEN EASIER TO DO.

JUNIOR NANNY

CHRIS JOHNSON worked at a residential nursery for the under-fives. One day, as Chris and another nurse, Anne, took the children out walking . . .

Look! That car's got ribbons on it. Why, Nurse Chris?

It's a wedding day car, Lucy. It brought the bride to the church and now it's waiting to take her and the bridegroom to what's called a reception.

Here they come! Oh! Isn't the bride lovely?

Want to see! Want to see the bride!

All right.

Those little girls are wearing pretty dresses, and they've got pretty flowers. Why are they holding the lady's dress, Nurse Chris?

That part of the dress is called the train, and the bridesmaids have to hold it up off the floor.

They saw the photographs being taken and stayed to watch the bride and bridegroom being showered with rice.

I wish I could be a bridesmaid.

So do I.

I don't want to wait lots of days to be a bridesmaid.

Neither do I, but I expect we'll have to.

Well, maybe you will be, one of these days. Right, time we were off home for tea.

Lucy, however, was not one to give up easily on an idea.

But, Nurse Chris, if you married Andrew, then Sara and I could be bridesmaids. You could get married on Saturday, because he doesn't go to school on Saturdays.

I've told you, Lucy — Andrew and I are just — er — friends. Anyway, it costs a lot of money to get married and we don't have enough.

Andrew, Chris's boyfriend, lived at a students' hostel next door to the nursery.

I think he could get the money and he loves you lots and lots. I know he does, because he calls you darling and . . .

Lucy! Go and wash your hands, ready for tea! At once!

62

63

64

Sent To Coventry

HAVE you ever been sent to Coventry? Well, I have. And I don't mean I was put on a train to the Midlands. When I first read about someone "being sent to Coventry" I had to ask Dad. He told me it meant not speaking to somebody; just ignoring them, as if they didn't exist.

Not much of a punishment, I thought — but that was before I sampled it for myself.

You see, it all started with this old man. Well, no... perhaps I'd better go back a bit further still, to put you in the picture.

Our family comes from the North of England, and I'm proud of it. But when Dad was promoted and sent by his firm to a small town not far from London, you'd have thought we were foreigners. The promotion meant a nice house and a private school for me, but from the very first moment I was like a fish out of water.

I'd come from a big school with noisy masses of people milling around and at first I'd been excited at going to a small school for girls only, like the ones I'd read about in some of Mum's old books.

Leaving on the first morning in my smart new uniform, I thought: "Patsy Dean, you're really getting somewhere at last." But then —

"Where do you come from?" the girls asked, in their southern voices.

When I said: "From up North... Lancashire," they fell about laughing.

"The lass cooms from oop North!" they mimicked.

Whenever I said "grass" or "castle," someone would be sure to giggle, but to me their "grawss" and "cawstle" sounded horribly affected.

They weren't all unpleasant, of course. In fact there was one quiet girl, Jane Matthews, who looked nice and was quite friendly, but

even she thought I was a bit peculiar when she asked me: "Patsy, can you ride?" and I said, "Yes, but I sold my bike before we came down here."

She thought I was trying to make a sharp, witty reply and she looked hurt, but I honestly didn't know she meant horses.

Briarwood, our school, was full of traditions and customs, and things that were "done" and "not done".

It was "done" to carry your books in a sort of leather bag in your arms, and "not done" to have an attache-case. It was "done" to wear your hat on the back of your head, and "not done" to have anything to do with members of the town Comprehensive.

So you can see I was always putting my foot in it, with my brand-new attaché-case and my hat pulled well down because it would have fallen off otherwise.

But I think the worst was this awful snooty thing about anybody who wasn't the right "clawss". That really got me.

In my first week at school, I came home one day and let Mum have the benefit of all I'd been bottling up.

"They're a lot of snobs, Mum. And the Head's the worst." I put on my best Briarwood accent. " 'I don't want to see any Briarwood gahl talking to boys in the street. I expect Briarwood gahls to remember the good name of the school and to behave properly in public, especially when in uniform.' "

"What makes her think there's anything special about that stuck-up lot?"

Mum's too meek for words.

"Try to be like the others, love," she said. "The school has a very good name, and Miss Leyton has to have rules, you know."

I threw my attaché-case down, and hated myself, because I knew there was a part of me that would have liked a leather bag to carry in my arms, and the self-confidence to wear my hat two sizes too small on the back of my head.

AS the days passed and I'd stopped being "that new girl from oop North", the girls didn't make fun of me so much, and Jane and I became really friendly.

The others might even have accepted me — until the episode of the old man.

The road where we lived was on the outskirts of the town and had houses on only one side. Opposite us was a little wood. Now, in autumn, it was damp, rather dreary, and not at all inviting.

I had noticed the old man several times. He was shabbily dressed, and he used to come up the hill pushing an empty wheelbarrow. He'd disappear into the wood and re-emerge half an hour later with the barrow piled high with leaf-mould, or sticks, and go trundling away down the hill again.

One damp day, when I was on my way home up the hill, I saw him coming down with his barrow. He was still some way off when he slipped on some fallen leaves and went down with a fearful bump on the pavement.

I sprinted up to the old man, who was sitting on the pavement looking dazed.

"Thank you, my dear," he said in a weak voice, as I pulled him to his feet.

He leant against me for a moment, and I could feel him shaking.

"Come into our house," I said. "You need to rest after a fall like that."

I helped him up the path and into the kitchen, then sat him on a chair.

Quickly I put the kettle on and made him a cup of tea.

"That was wonderful," he said. "I feel fine now. I'll be on my way."

"I'm coming, too," I insisted. "We don't want a repeat performance, do we?"

With me pushing the barrow and the old man hanging on to the handle, we made our way slowly down the hill.

"This is the place," he said, stopping outside a big house.

The front garden, even in autumn, was beautiful with dahlias and chrysanthemums,

and everything was neat and tidy. At the back, the vegetables were growing in neat rows and there was a big greenhouse filled with plants.

"I always collect the autumn leaves for compost," he said.

I looked round with awe.

"Do you keep all this huge garden going yourself?" I asked.

"It's a lot of work, but it's good work and I love it," he replied. "Thank you for your help, my dear. Come in and see me any time."

"Won't they mind at the house?" I asked doubtfully.

"They won't mind," he said, and waved to me as I walked out of the garden.

At school the next day, I wondered why some of the girls were

whispering and looking at me. I soon found out.

One of them, a real snooty character, came up to me and said: "If you must go out helping your scruffy old grandfather in broad daylight, Patsy Dean, don't do it in Briarwood uniform. You were seen, and you've let down the whole school. We have decided that you are to be sent to Coventry until you realise that we don't behave like that here."

She turned away, even before I could say: "But he's not my grandfather — he's just a poor old gardener who has to work much harder than any old man should."

I THOUGHT I wouldn't care about being left out, but I found it was hateful. I walked around at break; I moved between classes; and it was as though I didn't exist at all. I might have been invisible for all the notice that was taken of me — with one exception. Good old Jane smiled at me.

I hurried home from school on my own and met my old friend coming down the hill again with his barrow.

"Hello!" I said, dumped my case on top of the leaves, and, taking the handles from him, turned and wheeled the thing back to the big house.

I stayed and helped him add the leaves to his compost heap, then he took me through the greenhouse and showed me all the things he was growing in there. It was fascinating. You could tell he loved every plant, so I found myself getting more and more interested as he talked. At last I had to go, and ran home feeling more cheerful than I had all day.

Soon after tea, a ring came at the front door. I went and found Jane there, with a boy a year or so older.

"Hello, Patsy," said Jane. "I came to tell you I'm on your side. I shall talk to you, whatever they say. This is my brother, Pip. I've told him all about you, so now you have two friends."

"Three!" I said, and told them all about the old man and how hard he had to work.

"I'm keen on plants," said Pip. "Jane's useless in a garden, but perhaps I could help."

From then on, I didn't care about the Coventry thing. At school, I had Jane to talk to. After school, I used to meet Pip and we'd go along together and put in an hour with the old gardener, who told us to call him Fred.

No-one ever came out of the house to ask what we were doing there, and we really enjoyed helping. Both Pip and I learnt a lot about gardening — and about each other.

It soon got too dark in the evenings to do much, so we spent all Saturday afternoons there instead. This went on for weeks, and all that time I was given the cold shoulder at school.

Then they all began talking about Speech Day, when the Briarwood Governors came to give out the prizes. Parents were invited, and Mum bought a new outfit for the occasion. I hadn't the heart to tell her how I was being treated, and just hoped she wouldn't notice.

The great afternoon arrived. We filed into the Assembly Hall and took up our places behind the rows of parents. The Governors walked on to the platform — then I suddenly clutched Jane, who was sitting next to me.

"What on earth's the matter?" she whispered. "You've gone as white as a sheet!"

"On the platform!" I gasped. "It's my old gardener!"

"Don't be silly! That's the Chairman of the Governors, Sir Frederick Greenaway," said Jane under her breath.

I just sat there, hardly believing my eyes. For it was my old friend — dressed now in an expensive suit and wearing a late rose in his buttonhole.

The Head came on, then there was all the usual waffle and the presentation of all the Form prizes.

Then the Chairman stood up and said, in that voice I knew so well: "And now you are all wondering who is to receive the Governors' Special Prize for outstanding merit. This year we have decided to award it to a girl who for many weeks past has given up her spare time to help an old man of this town." I looked up and saw his eyes twinkling at me . "So will Patsy Dean step up to the platform?"

I went up in a daze to receive the thick illustrated book on gardening which he handed to me, and I caught a glimpse of Mum clapping away like mad.

When I would have walked off the platform, he stopped me and told everybody the whole story of our first meeting, finishing up — "and I hope she will forgive me for not telling her who I was.

"Her concern for someone she thought was overworked and infirm was too precious to spoil. She thought I was a gardener — as indeed I am, for I love my garden — and she has helped me with no thought of reward."

My face was burning as I went back to my place. At the end of the afternoon, a lot of the girls crowded round me, apologising for their behaviour.

"If only we'd known it was Sir Frederick," they said, as though that made all the difference. They wanted to be friendly now, but I knew who my real friends were — loyal Jane, "Fred" the gardener, and Pip.

It had been worth being sent to Coventry to have Pip as a special friend.

THE END

A PET SOCK for CHRISTMAS

Make a special Pet's Stocking for Christmas and fill it with all the little extras she or he likes.

If you don't have an old ankle sock, or can't get one from anyone in your family, make your own.

A Pet Sock can be made from any material that won't tear easily and will stitch by hand or machine. It should measure about 205 mm. (8 inches) from toe to heel along the bottom of the sock, and 125 mm. (5 inches) across the middle of the foot part, and be 230 mm. (9 inches) from ankle top downwards at the heel end. The front of the ankle measures 100 mm. (4 inches) downwards with about 125 mm. (5 inches) opening at the top.

When stitching, try to allow up to 13 mm. (half an inch) for seam width on all seams.

Suggestions for filling your Pet Socks.

For Dogs:— Doggie chocs, condition powders, yeast tablets, dog shampoo, bone-shaped biscuits and other dog treats, grooming brush/comb, nail clippers, collar/lead, choke chain, name tag/disc. Plus anything else that won't melt and will fit in.

For Cats:— Much the same as dogs. Also, flea collar, toy mouse, small tin of favourite food, two packets of worm tablets (1 for roundworm, 1 for tapeworm) a special grooming glove for removing loose hair easily. Plus whatever else you can think of that your cat would like.

For rabbits, hamsters, guinea pigs, mice, etc., you can buy an assortment of *small* quantities of their food, such as rabbit pellets, bran, flaked maize, crushed oats. Also make up your own idea of their special treat, plus clean, dry, carrots, very small apples, and shelled hazelnuts — but no nuts for rabbits!

You can get special treats to hang in the cage for most of them, as you can for budgies, canaries, parrots, etc. A must for caged birds is cuttlefish.

If you haven't a pet, but know someone who has — perhaps an elderly person — why not give *their* pet a Christmas Sock? I'm sure both pet and owner would be delighted with it.

SCHOOLGIRL VET

KAY BURROWS loved all animals and hoped one day to become a vet like her brother, David. Their mother went into hospital for a minor operation and they were told — sooner than they expected — that she was to be allowed home.

Normally, the doctor would have preferred your mother to stay a little longer, but she's been fretting so much that we think she will recover more quickly with you — if you can cope.

My job takes me out on emergency calls at all hours — but Kay will be in charge, and she'll do the job well, I'm sure.

Once home—

It's wonderful to be home. I just felt I would never start to get better while we were parted.

We understand.

Kay's mother made rapid progress.

Are you taking your tablets regularly, Mum?

Of course. Don't fuss! Anyway, being together again is all the medicine I really need.

Within a few days Mrs Burrows had made such good progress that Kay felt able to accept an invitation to spend the afternoon with a friend.

Mum, would you be all right on your own for an hour or two? Tessa works at Partlett Hall and she's asked me to ride over. The family are away and it would be a great chance to see the house.

Of course, dear. Have a lovely time. I'll be fine.

Partlett Hall was an historic show place, but it was closed to the public while the family were abroad.

How super to work in a place like this. I've loved seeing the house. But I mustn't leave Mum alone too long.

I'll walk round to the stables with you. Ah! Here comes the tanker to deliver a load of oil for the central heating.

Early the following morning there was an agitated telephone call from Tessa.

Kay! Something dreadful has happened here during the night to one of the swans! I think it's dying! It could be all my fault!

I'll tell David. He hasn't started his morning calls yet. We'll both come over.

69

At Partlett Hall—

What happened?

Oil's been leaking out of the storage tank into the lake all night. One of the delivery men must have left a tap loose.

Nobody could blame you for that, surely?

Oh, but they could. I was left in charge. I should have checked that the men had done their job properly.

The sooner we get that bird into the surgery for treatment, the better.

Kay wrapped the rescued swan in a blanket.

In the surgery store we've got a drum of that chemical stuff that the bird hospital uses on oiled-up sea birds.

I'll send an assistant over to spray the slick with it.

They drove to the surgery with the swan.

You're doing a great job.

I've got the feathers clean, but the poor thing is terribly weak. We must save it.

The trouble is that getting it clean is not the main problem. It's oil it swallowed, trying to preen its feathers, that has made it so ill. The bird hospital is tackling similar cases all the time. I'm sure they're help.

At the bird hospital—

You've done a marvellous cleaning-up job, Kay.

But it's still a very sick bird.

We've cured worse. With so much oil spillage on local beaches, we've gained plenty of experience.

We'll have to get rid of all the oil it's swallowed.

And feed it artificially for a few days until it is strong enough to feed itself.

Thanks. We'll leave it in your care until the weekend.

But when they returned at the weekend—

It's made no progress at all!

We can't understand it. By now, it should be well on the way to recovery.

It makes no effort. If we didn't feed it by hand, it would starve.

71

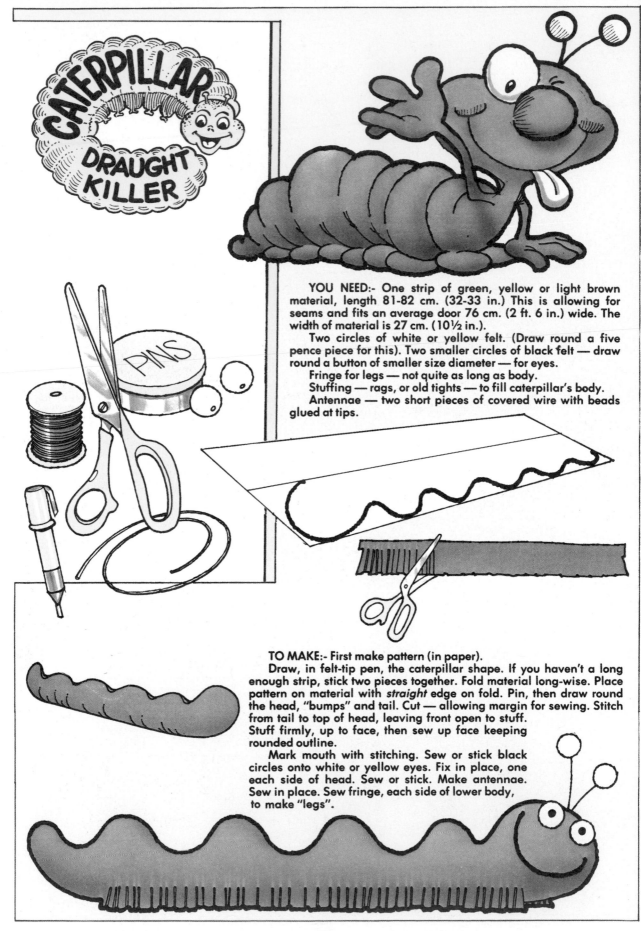

YOU NEED:- One strip of green, yellow or light brown material, length 81-82 cm. (32-33 in.) This is allowing for seams and fits an average door 76 cm. (2 ft. 6 in.) wide. The width of material is 27 cm. (10½ in.).

Two circles of white or yellow felt. (Draw round a five pence piece for this). Two smaller circles of black felt — draw round a button of smaller size diameter — for eyes.

Fringe for legs — not quite as long as body.

Stuffing — rags, or old tights — to fill caterpillar's body.

Antennae — two short pieces of covered wire with beads glued at tips.

TO MAKE:- First make pattern (in paper).

Draw, in felt-tip pen, the caterpillar shape. If you haven't a long enough strip, stick two pieces together. Fold material long-wise. Place pattern on material with *straight* edge on fold. Pin, then draw round the head, "bumps" and tail. Cut — allowing margin for sewing. Stitch from tail to top of head, leaving front open to stuff. Stuff firmly, up to face, then sew up face keeping rounded outline.

Mark mouth with stitching. Sew or stick black circles onto white or yellow eyes. Fix in place, one each side of head. Sew or stick. Make antennae. Sew in place. Sew fringe, each side of lower body, to make "legs".

Cora Cupid

CORA CARTER, of Palewell Comprehensive, thought of herself as a born matchmaker, often with dire results. One day . . . .

Hi, Jenny! You don't look too happy.

I'm not, Cora. I've fallen out with Tony.

Never mind, you'll soon make things up.

But it won't be in time for the Disco Championship on Saturday. Tony was my partner.

I'm going in to see if Tony's inside.

I'm sure we'll find Tony in here, and he'll be feeling just as miserable as you are.

But when the girls got inside, Tony had already found himself a new partner, Pat Doig.

Oh, no! He's found another partner!

Oops! This might be more difficult than I thought!

Come back, Jenny!

Jenny turned and ran.

Sob! I can't bear to watch him being so happy with someone else!

73

Cora caught up with Jenny farther down the street.

Sorry, Cora, but it was such a shock. It wouldn't be quite so bad if I could only find a new partner — but the Disco Competition is on Saturday, and this is Thursday.

Leave it to me, Jenny. I'll find you a partner, somehow.

Later, when Cora was with her own boyfriend, Phil—

. . . and there I was racing up the left wing, when . . . Cora! You're not listening to me!

Sorry, Phil, but I have a whopping big problem. I must find a male experienced disco dancer before tomorrow night.

I've got it! I've got it! I don't have time to explain just now, Phil — but meet me at the corner of Brown Street at eight o'clock!

At home, Cora got busy.

Then, at 8 p.m.—

Here's a map, Phil. You can do the south side of the town and I'll do the north. Check all the discos on this list and see if you can find a suitable male dancer. I'll 'phone you later when I'm finished my list.

OK, Cora.

Cora and Phil visited many discos.

Fashion Quiz

The world of ladies' fashions is constantly changing. See if you can identify the styles and fashion accessories shown here. If you are stuck, you'll find the answers below.

1. This girl wears the correct gear for a popular form of exercise. What is it?

2. These elegant, trouser-suited girls of the 1960's are wearing a type of feathery neckwear. What is it called?

3. What was the name given to this ankle-length fashion?

4. This fetching lace bridal dress is modelled on the "flapper" style that dates back to when?

5. A smart winter coat based on a South American cloak. Name it.

6. All the rage in the early 1970's, what were these shorts called?

ANSWERS 1. Jogging; 2. Boa; 3. Maxi; 4. 1920's; 5. Poncho; 6. Hot Pants.

76

COMMUNITY NURSE

CAROL HARVEY, a community nurse, based at the Daleport and District Health Centre, treated patients in their own homes. One afternoon, Carol arrived at the outskirts of the town to visit two patients, Alan and David Roberts, who had measles, but found their mother unconscious.

What happened, Alan?

Mum had fetched our dinner tray, then the 'phone rang, and she must have hurried and tripped or something.

Is she . . . is she dead?

No, David. She's taken a bad bump on the head, though. She'll have to go to hospital. I'll 'phone for an ambulance.

When the ambulance left—

The boys have had a nasty shock. I'll put them to bed and 'phone the school to ask for their sister to be sent home. Angela is almost seventeen...old enough to cope.

Angela was home within the hour.

Hello, Nurse. Is there any news from the hospital about Mum?

Not yet. They'll have to take X-rays and do some tests. Take your coat off and sit down, Angela. I'll pour you a cup of tea.

My father is at sea with the Royal Navy. He should be told about Mum's accident, but I don't know how to go about it.

I'll see to it, once we have definite news from the hospital.

78

MAKE USE OF THOSE OUT-OF-DATE CATALOGUES WITH THIS FASCINATING NEW CRAFT!

THE CATALOGUES ARE YOUR TREASURE-HOUSE FOR FURNISHINGS AND EQUIPMENT OF ALL KINDS. TO MAKE YOUR HOUSE, YOU NEED THE LID OF A CARDBOARD BOX ROUGHLY THE SIZE SHOWN BELOW.

MAKE A ROOF FROM A STRIP OF STOUT CARD 1 CM WIDER THAN THE BOX WIDTH, AND FASTEN WITH STICKY-TAPE. CUT TWO CARD STRIPS TO FIT ACROSS THE LID, MAKE SLOTS HALF-WAY IN EACH, SLOT TOGETHER AND FASTEN IN PLACE WITH TAPE.

SET UP HOUSE

DECORATE THE WALLS, OR PASTE ON SUITABLE PAPER. NEXT, GLUE ON ITEMS THAT ARE TO BE FLAT ON THE WALLS, SUCH AS WINDOWS AND DOORS, ALL OBTAINABLE FROM YOUR CATALOGUES. CARPETS ON THE FLOORS ARE CUT FROM MATERIAL SCRAPS, GLUED DOWN.

ROOF — 15 CM

20 CM

13 CM

3 CM

SLOT

SLOT

FINALLY, SELECT YOUR FURNITURE AND OTHER HOUSEHOLD ITEMS — CLOCKS, MIRRORS, PICTURES, LAMPS — AND GLUE THEM INTO PLACE. NATURALLY, EVERYTHING MUST BE OF A SUITABLE SIZE AND SCALE - THEY'RE ALL IN YOUR CATALOGUES BUT DON'T EXPECT THEM TO JUMP OUT AT YOU.... YOU HAVE TO SEARCH FOR THEM - THAT'S WHERE THE FUN AND THE CRAFT COME IN!

A REAL EYE-CATCHER TO HANG IN YOUR ROOM.

BRILLIANT! THIS GRANDFATHER CLOCK IS JUST THE RIGHT SIZE!

PASTE THE ITEMS TO CARD, THEN OFFSET THEM FROM THE WALL BY GLUING SCRAPS OF CARD AS SHOWN HERE, SO THAT SOME ITEMS STAND FURTHER INTO THE ROOM THAN OTHERS, GIVING A THREE-DIMENSIONAL EFFECT.

Jest-a-minute

Q. WHAT DO YOU CALL A BAD-TEMPERED BEAR WITH COTTON-WOOL IN ITS EARS?

A. ANYTHING YOU LIKE. IT CAN'T HEAR YOU.

MAN: "I'VE A NASTY PAIN IN MY RIGHT ARM, DOCTOR."
DOCTOR: "I SHOULDN'T WORRY — IT'S JUST OLD AGE."
MAN: "WELL, WHY DOESN'T MY OTHER ARM HURT? I'VE HAD THAT ONE JUST AS LONG!"

I WISH I HAD YOUR PICTURE— THE ONE TAKEN WITH YOUR CATS— I'D HANG IT IN THE GARDEN SHED TO SCARE AWAY THE RATS.

CHEEP JOKE!

Q. WHY DID THE BURGLAR TAKE A SHOWER?
A. HE WANTED A CLEAN GET-AWAY!

HOW MANY PUPILS WORK IN YOUR CLASS?

ABOUT HALF OF THEM.

A MAN CAME TO THE POLICE STATION AND COMPLAINED: "I HAVE TWO BROTHERS AND WE ALL LIVE IN THE ONE ROOM. ONE OF MY BROTHERS HAS FIVE CATS AND THE OTHER HAS FIVE DOGS. THE SMELL IS TERRIBLE. CAN YOU DO SOMETHING ABOUT IT?"

"YOU COULD OPEN THE WINDOW," SUGGESTED THE POLICEMAN.

"WHAT, AND LOSE ALL MY TWENTY BUDGIES?" SAID THE MAN.

A MAN IN A BUS SPOKE TO THE YOUNG GIRL SITTING OPPOSITE HIM.

"DO YOU REALISE," HE SAID, "THAT YOU'RE READING YOUR MAGAZINE UPSIDE DOWN?"

"OF COURSE I REALISE IT," REPLIED THE GIRL. "DO YOU THINK IT'S EASY?"

PETAL FUN

A SINGLE TULIP PETAL

MAKE YOUR PATTERNS OR PICTURES BY GLUING THE MATERIAL ONTO CARD — PLAIN WHITE, COLOURED, OR BLACK... ALL GIVE INDIVIDUAL EFFECTS. DON'T TRY TO COPY THE FLOWERS THE PETALS CAME FROM, BUT CREATE EXOTIC BLOSSOMS OF YOUR OWN. OURS (ABOVE) WAS MADE FROM PETALS, LEAF, STEM AND STAMENS OF AN ORDINARY TULIP.

MAKE OTHER PICS AS SHOWN BELOW, USING FULL PETALS FOR INSTANCE AS IN THE CRINOLINE LADY'S SKIRT, AND CUTTING PARTS OF PETALS FOR ALL THE OTHER SHAPES.

PRESS THE COMPLETED PICTURES BETWEEN BOOKS AND NEWSPAPERS A FEW MINUTES WHILE THE GLUE IS DRYING.

COLLECT YOUR PETALS — PREFERABLY LARGE, COLOURFUL ONES... TULIP, ROSE, DAFFODIL, ETC — PLUS SOME LEAVES, STEMS AND STAMENS.

IF YOU HAVEN'T A PROPER FLOWER-PRESS, LAY THEM FLAT BETWEEN NEWSPAPERS AND PRESS UNDER A PILE OF BOOKS FOR SEVERAL DAYS.

IF THE STEMS ARE THICK, SLICE THEM DOWN THE CENTRE WITH A PENKNIFE.

ROSE.

DAFFODIL.

A FLOWER-PRESS.

MAKE OTHER PICS, TOO.

DÉCOUPAGE

Découpage is a grand-sounding word which simply means "cutting out". It is a very effective way of decorating practically anything, from a piece of furniture to an ash-tray. It probably started in the eighteenth century, when it was very fashionable for the aristocracy to buy Chinese or Japanese furniture. There was such a demand for it that the craftsmen in this country were forced to copy oriental designs on furniture. They did this by sticking engravings on the furniture before applying a coat of lacquer. Découpage became a very popular pastime, both in this country and in France. It is a hobby that is both absorbing and inexpensive.

You will need:-
A lid from a large tin
A small amount of emulsion paint
A little clear varnish
A sheet of decorated wrapping paper, magazine page, or similar, with design of your choice.

1. Paint the lid carefully. You will probably need to give it two coats to cover it evenly. 2. Cut out the design you have chosen and stick it in place. 3. Give it two coats of varnish — make sure the first is completely dry before applying the second coat. Boxes, lamps, waste-paper bins can all be given a new lease of life in this simple way.

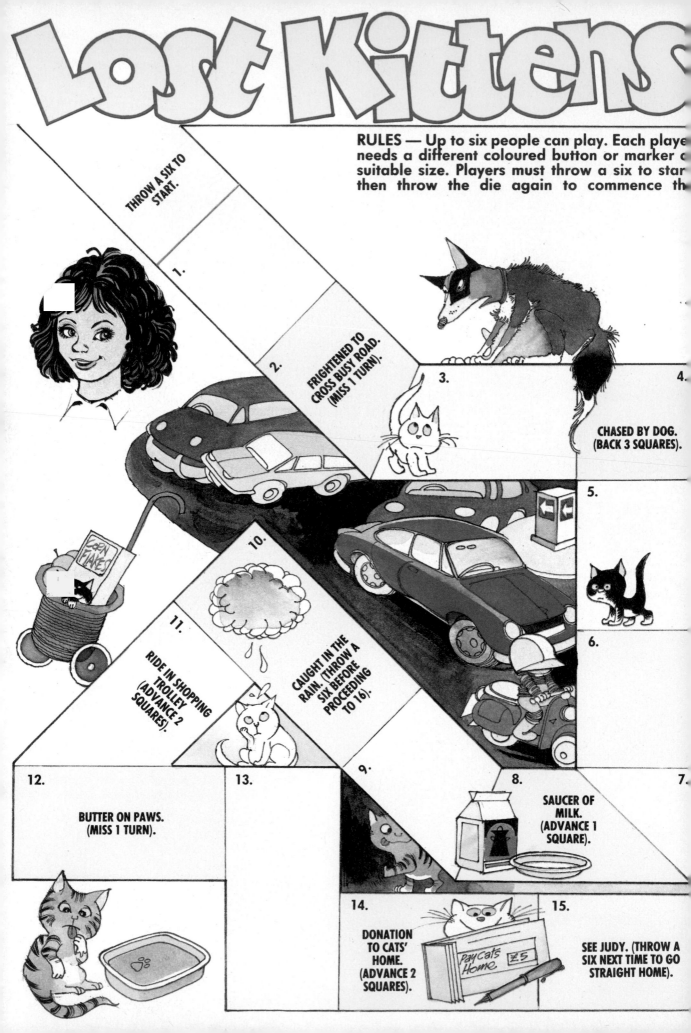

Lost Kittens

RULES — Up to six people can play. Each player needs a different coloured button or marker of suitable size. Players must throw a six to start, then throw the die again to commence the

THROW A SIX TO START.

1.

2. FRIGHTENED TO CROSS BUSY ROAD. (MISS 1 TURN).

3.

4. CHASED BY DOG. (BACK 3 SQUARES).

5.

6.

7.

8. SAUCER OF MILK. (ADVANCE 1 SQUARE).

9.

10. CAUGHT IN THE RAIN. (THROW A SIX BEFORE PROCEEDING TO 16).

11. RIDE IN SHOPPING TROLLEY (ADVANCE 2 SQUARES).

12. BUTTER ON PAWS. (MISS 1 TURN).

13.

14. DONATION TO CATS' HOME. (ADVANCE 2 SQUARES).

15. SEE JUDY. (THROW A SIX NEXT TIME TO GO STRAIGHT HOME).

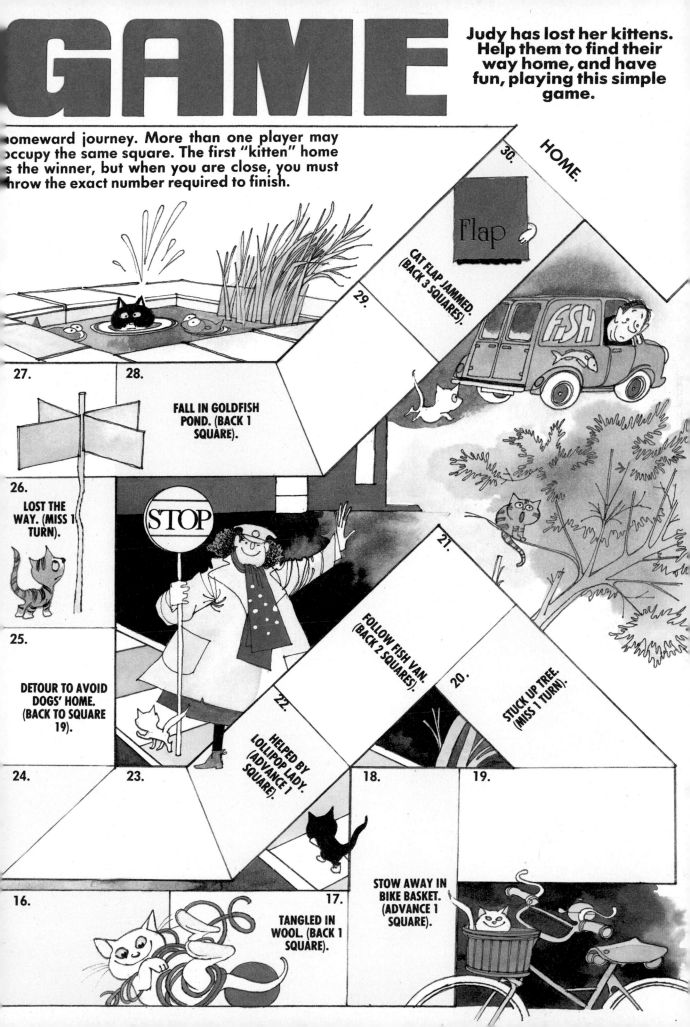

GAME

Judy has lost her kittens. Help them to find their way home, and have fun, playing this simple game.

...homeward journey. More than one player may ...occupy the same square. The first "kitten" home ...s the winner, but when you are close, you must ...hrow the exact number required to finish.

HOME.

30.

Flap

CAT FLAP JAMMED. (BACK 3 SQUARES).

29.

FISH

27.

28.

FALL IN GOLDFISH POND. (BACK 1 SQUARE).

26. **LOST THE WAY. (MISS 1 TURN).**

STOP

25.

DETOUR TO AVOID DOGS' HOME. (BACK TO SQUARE 19).

21.

FOLLOW FISH VAN. (BACK 2 SQUARES).

20. **STUCK UP TREE. (MISS 1 TURN).**

22. **HELPED BY LOLLIPOP LADY. (ADVANCE 1 SQUARE).**

24.

23.

18.

19.

16.

17. **TANGLED IN WOOL. (BACK 1 SQUARE).**

STOW AWAY IN BIKE BASKET. (ADVANCE 1 SQUARE).

Stookie

When I was five weeks old, I decided to explore the wood. Flying was easy, but no-one had told me how to stop. I crashed onto the road and hurt my leg. At the Wildlife Rescue Centre a vet put my leg in plaster, and Mrs Christie, who looked after me, explained that the Centre was a hospital for injured birds and animals.

HI! My name is Stookie and I'm a tawny owl. I used to live in a big chestnut tree, in a hole in a broken branch. It was cosy there, snuggled up to my fluffy brother, waiting for our parents to bring us food.

I made friends with Coco, a spaniel puppy. When he was sleepy he cuddled up to me, just like my brother did — but he wasn't too keen on letting me share his food!

It was a bit difficult flying then, because the weight of the plaster held me down, so I thought it would be a good idea if I could ride on the lawnmower.

Then I found this perch in the vegetable garden. It was just the right size and not too high. Mrs Christie said I would be quite useful there if I frightened away the birds who had been eating her seeds.

It was lucky that she had left her washing out. I, being a wise owl, found it. That towel was just what I needed to dry my feet.

It was hard work being a scarecrow and I really needed a bath to cool me down. This bird bath was a bit small, but Mrs Christie said I couldn't have any more water because I wasn't to get my plaster wet.

I was very brave when the vet came to take my plaster off, and - hoo, hoo - now I am able to fly much higher. Landing on the caravan wasn't popular. Mrs Christie said I sounded like a whole army of soldiers wearing hobnail boots, marching backwards and forwards across the roof.

Now that my leg is better, I can catch my own food. I live in the wood beside the Rescue Centre, and I hunt at night. I have very good hearing, and, with my big, round eyes can see mice running through long grass when it is so dark that *you* couldn't see anything at all.

I am very tired by morning and I fall asleep, leaning against the smooth grey bark of the beech tree.

APOLLODORUS

Apollodorus is a pig.
The trouble is, he's far too big.
He can't fit into any sty —
The farmer's had a real good try.

"Oh, put him in the cowshed! There's
An empty stall right next to Claire's!"
In went the farmer — name of Reg —
But, dang it all — that pig got wedged!

Reg scratched his head, then said, "O' course!
I'll put 'im with the old brown 'orse!"
The horse was old, and stiff with gout —
But he soon chased the big pig out!

"I know — the barn!" cried Reg's
    son.
"That's large enough for *anyone*!
Yes, that'll get him out the way!"
But that fat pig just ate the hay.

By now he'd reached enormous size,
And Reg no longer felt so wise.
"There's only one thing for it — yus,
We'll 'ave to 'ave 'im in with us!"

That pig he sits in the best
    chair,
Right by the fire. Just see him
    glare
If Reg's wife is late with tea,
Or someone switches off TV!

A TOY CLOWN TO MAKE

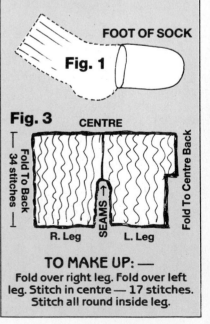

TIE

ARM

Fig. 2

LEG

MATERIALS NEEDED

Oddments of coloured wool — for clown's garments; red and black wool, or felt, for face features; wool for hair; a white sock for body; felt for shoe soles; circle of flat foam, covered with white material, for face; felt, or material with felt pom-poms for hat; strip of ribbon or other material for neck frill; stuffing — cotton-wool is best.

TO MAKE BODY

Cut off foot of sock to heel. (See figure 1.) Stuff to rounded toe-top. Sew at bottom. Tie cotton at place where neck should be (figure 2.) Make legs from rib of sock (2 oblongs approx. 114 x 50 mm [4½ x 2 in.].) Seam up long sides, making tubes. Sew at end, then stuff. Add felt soles. Tie at ankles. Attach legs to body. Make arms same way. If not enough sock material left, use any material and round at hands.

Cut circle of white material. (Draw round rim of large cup.) Put foam circle (slightly smaller) inside. Run thread all round material and draw up slightly. Pencil in features first — then embroider, or felt applique, red nose, mouth and black eyes.

HAIR

On our model, it is worked in loops all over head, with extra sideburns . Alternatively, make a skein of wool, winding round a card 127 mm. (5 in.) deep. Secure one side by sewing, then cut across the other. Attach to head by the sewn-together part.

HAT

Make cone by drawing a half circle. (Try a tea-plate for size). Sew at sides. Stiffen inside with a lining — or some stuffing. Sew firmly to hair.

CLOWN'S GARMENT

In 4 ply wool, cast on 34 sts. on No. 8 needles. Knit in stripes of garter stitch. (Plain each row). K 34 rows. (No need to cut ends, just bring up colours — at same end — 2 rows of each colour.)

Then cast off 17 stitches. Knit remaining 17 stitches for 2 rows, then cast on 17 stitches. K another 34 rows. Cast off 17 sts. Knit 2 more rows on the 17 left. Cast off. Make up garment. See directions on figure No. 4.

Put on body, gathering top of trousers at neck.

SLEEVES

Knit 17 stitches in same stripes for 32 rows. Sew into tubes. Slide on to arms. Attach securely at shoulders.

Run gathering thread at edge of neck frill. Draw up and fix round neck.

FOOT OF SOCK

Fig. 1

Fig. 3

CENTRE

Fold To Back
34 stitches

Fold To Centre Back

R. Leg   SEAMS   L. Leg

TO MAKE UP: —

Fold over right leg. Fold over left leg. Stitch in centre — 17 stitches. Stitch all round inside leg.

95

THE card shot through the letter-box and fluttered to the floor just as I came tearing down the stairs with only ten minutes to spare before the school bus left.

"Post!" I yelled, pulling on my blazer and peering at my hair in the hall mirror.

Mum came bustling through from the kitchen.

"You've just got time for a slice of toast, Fran," she told me fussily. "You can't go to school without some breakfast."

"Goodness!" I said crossly. "I shan't starve, you know!"

But I dashed into the kitchen all the same and crammed half a slice in my mouth, because Mum's as stubborn as a mule and sometimes it's quicker to do as she says than argue.

"Anyway, love, this is for you," Mum said, following me in. "It's addressed to 'F. Tucker, 16 Willows End.'"

I almost snatched the card from her. For me? I never got any letters . . . well, hardly ever. Whatever could it be? I turned it over...and nearly fainted from shock.

"We are very pleased to be able to tell you," it read, "that you have won the first prize in our recent competition. We congratulate you and hope that you will be able to attend a small ceremony at which you will be presented with the prize."

"A prize?" I muttered in a daze. Then it suddenly struck home. "A prize! Mum, I've won a prize!" I shouted, waving the card at her. "I've actually won a prize!"

And I sat down heavily on the nearest chair, dislodging the cat and knocking over a cereal packet with my elbow.

Which competition was it? I thought hard. Was it the holiday camp one or the teenage wardrobe? No, they were over ages ago. I glanced at the calendar. Gosh, it could only be the —

"Pony competition!" I shouted out loud. "Mum, I've won a pony!"

Mum had to sit down then.

"I just can't take it in," she said. "Are you sure, love? It doesn't say anything on the card; just a London address."

"It's the only competition I've entered recently," I explained. "We'll know all about it when they send a letter."

"Yes, it says they'll be getting in touch about arrangements," Mum said, reading it all over again.

Absent-mindedly I munched a piece of toast as I thought about my good luck. How fantastic, how fabulous, it all was. I'd never won anything before in my life and yet the number of competitions I'd entered was nobody's business. But now I was rewarded with a pony of my own. I could hardly believe it.

"You will let me keep it, Mum?" I blurted out anxiously. "I mean, Dad won't —"

"Not to worry, Fran," Mum said, laughing. "I bet your dad will be tickled pink. At least it will save on riding lessons, and I don't expect Mr Davis at the farm would charge an awful lot for keep. After all, your dad does him a lot of favours over the farm machinery."

"I just can't wait to tell him, and Eddie, too. Gosh, he'll really get a surprise when he comes home! I may even have the pony by then."

Eddie is my elder brother. He's quite nice, really, as brothers go, and since he'd been away in France on an exchange visit, I had missed him quite a bit.

Well, by the time I got over the shock and Mum and I had had a natter, I'd long since missed the bus, so I was late for school. The Head was quite decent about it, though, and even said she thought she'd be late turning up herself if she ever won a competition.

And the gang nearly went berserk when I told them,

because they'd gone in for just as many comps as I had and never been half as lucky.

"Trust you, Fran," Cathy said enviously. "I thought I was lucky when I won that oil painting set last year, but a pony . . ."

"At least we can all share it," I offered happily. "After all, we can all ride, so I'll draw up a proper rota, I promise. But I'll have to get some decent riding kit," I added thoughtfully. "Wellies and jeans may be OK for an hour at the riding stables every Saturday, but not for a proper pony owner."

To my relief, even Dad agreed with this when we were discussing it later that day.

"Don't go too mad, though," he warned. "You've got a hat, so you just need boots and jodhpurs." Then catching sight of my face he added teasingly: "And have you ever thought about a hacking jacket?"

"Dad, you're the greatest!" I told him, and I hugged him hard before hurrying upstairs to make out a list. Apart from the gear, there were all sorts of other things I'd need, and I couldn't wait to write it all down.

"I'm sure it said that the tack was part of the prize," I muttered as I rummaged about in my desk drawer. "Oh blow! Where is that piece of paper?"

But though I searched and searched, I couldn't find the page from the magazine with the competition details.

"Never mind," I told myself. "I expect I'll get a letter soon." And I settled down happily to make lists of things like dandy brushes and body brushes and all the interesting things that go to make up the pony world.

BY the time Saturday came, the list was longer than one of Dad's best runner beans so, deciding a bit of discretion was needed, I made a shorter one with just the clothes on it. That did the trick.

"Best pop into town and get that little lot today," Dad said generously. "Ten to one they'll only let you know at the last minute when the ceremony is going to be. If you're all prepared, you can wear them and look the part."

"Very nice," Mum said later when I paraded downstairs in my new finery.

"Just the job," Dad smiled.

"Wait till Eddie sees me," I giggled. "He won't be able to call me his little sister any more."

I wasn't exaggerating, either, because the riding gear made me look much older–especially with my hair swept up under my hat.

"Eddie will have the surprise of his life if he comes home and finds I've acquired a pony in the three weeks he's been gone," I joked.

But it wasn't Eddie who got the surprise in the end — at least, not in the way I meant it then. It was me.

The longed-for letter came first post on Monday, still not with many details but telling me all I wanted to know, anyway.

"We have decided to come to your home town for your convenience and, of course, it will be an open air presentation," it explained. "So, please could you and your parents come to the forecourt of Smith's garage at midday on Saturday? We shall then, of course, require your parents' written consent for you to accept the prize."

"Why not the riding stables?" I wondered idly. But then I remembered that the garage was right opposite the book-shop that sold the magazine that the competition was in.

The only thing that bothered me a bit was that the letter started with Dear Mr Tucker.

"I suppose they think I'm a boy," I told Mum. "What with my name being Frances. But it can't make any difference, can it?"

Saturday took ages to come, but in the end it arrived along with a letter from Eddie warning Mum that he and his French pal, Pierre, were expecting to arrive sometime too.

"Perfect timing," I laughed, as Dad drove Mum and me through the town to the garage.

Some of the gang were there already – all of them armed with copies of the horsey magazine that had sponsored the competition, and all dressed in horsey type clothes. In fact, there was quite a crowd, what with hangers-on as well.

Happily I marched forward to the group of people who I guessed must be the competition sponsors. They were all dressed very nattily in suits, which surprised me a bit, as I'd imagined they'd be in horsey togs, too.

"Good morning," I said, cheerily. "I'm Fran Tucker, come to collect my prize."

Well, if I'd said I was Dracula come for half a pint of best blood, they couldn't have

looked more astonished. Their mouths dropped open and there was a nasty silence. At last the one in the spotted tie managed, "Tucker? Not Mr Tucker?"

What a dumb question, I thought. But I just smiled even more brightly and said; "Well, I guess you were mistaken over the Frances bit. Lots of people do get mixed up," I added kindly. "But I'm Frances not Francis."

"Actually . . . er Miss . . . er Frances —" Spotty tie struggled and gave up. He looked round helplessly at the other people in the group and I suddenly realised they were all men.

What's happened to Women's Lib, I asked myself? But I didn't really care. As long as I got my pony, I didn't care if it was a presentation committee of Buddhist monks.

A man with a ginger moustache stepped forward then.

"Well — er — Miss Tucker, I think there's been some sort of mistake. You see, you couldn't possibly have won this prize. You're too young."

"Of course I won it," I began, wildly searching in my pocket for the card and letter. But before I could show them he took my arm and pointed. "That's the prize, my dear," he explained. "Surely you didn't enter a competition for that?"

I stared stupidly at the beautiful new shiny motor bike standing in the corner of the forecourt. Its metal gleamed in the sun and it looked ready to burst into life.

"But . . . but I thought I'd won a pony," was all I could manage to say, then I promptly burst into tears.

Well, of course, there was a frightful to-do then. Mum and Dad had joined me and the audience crowded round, too. There was so much noise and confusion that I felt I wanted to crawl away into a hole and hide. But I couldn't run away. I had to stick it out and hear how I'd misread the address, and that it was the initial E with the bottom bit almost too faint to see, and not F for Frances at all.

"Then it's E. Tucker who won the prize?" Dad asked. "E. Tucker of Willows End?"

"That's right," agreed spotty tie. "And if it's not you," he told Dad, "It's —"

"My son," said Dad. "D'you hear that, Mum? It's Eddie who's won the competition."

Mum smiled faintly, and I sniffed loudly and dried my eyes.

"Then it wasn't anything to do with the pony competition at all?" I hiccuped.

"No, Fran," said Dad, giving my arm a squeeze. "You jumped the gun a bit. I know it's been a nasty disappointment, but what you've never had you won't miss, you know. And think how excited Eddie will be."

And he was, too. He was over the moon with joy.

"As soon as I've passed my test, Fran," he promised, "you shall be my first pillion passenger."

"This gear's not going to be any good for that sort of riding," I said gloomily, glancing down at the riding outfit which I hadn't had the heart to change out of all day.

Eddie's exchange pal looked at me then, his eyes as dark as his hair.

"But Francees," he said in a film-star-type accent." You look veree nice in your 'orse riding clothes. Perhaps you will permit me to take you riding while I visit here with you?"

"He's at it already," teased Eddie, winking at me. "You'll have to watch Pierre with all that continental charm, Fran." And he and Mum and Dad laughed at the thought of anyone using charm on me.

But Pierre only smiled at me and raised his eyebrows questioningly.

"Oui, merci beaucoup," I told him, shyly trying out my third year French. "I'd like that."

Perhaps it was just as well I hadn't won the pony, I thought to myself. After all, there were other things in life besides horses. And suddenly I had a sneaky feeling that I was going to get quite interested in French in the next few weeks.

THE END

BIRD PUDDING

A winter landscape, with snow-tipped branches glistening in the sunshine, looks so pretty — but spare a thought for the birds.

It is not a pretty time for them. With the ground frozen hard as rock, and sometimes snow covered, food becomes increasingly difficult to find. This is when you should put out more food and tit-bits for the birds. The extra supply can really be a lifesaver. Here are some useful hints and tips for food, drink and shelter for birds from H. J. Heinz.

FOOD:—

Why not make your own bird pudding? The most important ingredient is fat — needed to keep birds warm, as well as bind the other pudding goodies together. You can use melted dripping from Mum's grill pan, lard, suet, or margarine . . . the birds aren't fussy. The safest way to melt the fat is to put it in an old cup or jug and place this in a large bowl of hot water.

As for the other ingredients, choose from porridge oats, crushed cereal flakes, chopped unsalted nuts, dried fruit or apple pips. Mix three or four ingredients in a bowl and pour over just enough melted fat to moisten the mixture, so your bird pudding will be nice and crumbly.

Allow the pudding to set in the bowl, ready to be crumbled onto your bird table. You may make lots of smaller bird puddings, using a selection of moulds. Ideal moulds include any screw-tops from produce jars and bottles. You can cut short lengths of string to drop into the mix, leaving one end free. When your pudding is set, a few minutes' warm-up on a warm surface will loosen it, complete with the length of string to hang it up. The hanging pudding will provide a good meal for the birds and give you fun watching their acrobatics.

DRINK:—

As well as food, birds need water for drinking and keeping their feathers clean, so give your flying visitors a supply of water. Remember to check it every day to make sure that the water is not frozen.

SHELTER:—

Second to food and water for bird winter survival is a form of shelter. It doesn't have to be an expensive bird table — a makeshift one will do just as well. For instance, you will find that any four-legged low stool proves very handy. All you need to do is to turn it upside down and nail a wooden board to the four legs, so that the board becomes the roof of the bird table. Birds will then be able to fly inside during the bad weather and perch underneath. The bird table can either be set in a sheltered place on the ground or nailed onto a broom handle, so that it stands several feet above the ground.

ORPHAN ISLAND

THERE was a shortage of children on Freeman Island and its young schoolteacher, Chris Warren, persuaded the council, headed by Dame Isobel Freeman, to let her bring orphans to the island. One afternoon, when the scheme had been in operation almost a year, Chris took the children to the woods to look for nature specimens. Chris paid particular attention to nine-year-old Jenny Reid, the latest orphan to arrive on the island.

That's the fattest frog I've ever seen, Jenny. I reckon he thinks a lot of himself. See how he's puffing his cheeks out? Doesn't he look funny?

What a sad little face Jenny has. I haven't seen her smile in the three days she's been on the island.

Miss Chris! Miss Chris! Get the kids moving — out of the woods!

Part of the wood is on fire. It's a fair distance off, but the wind could spread the flames in this direction.

I'll round the children up. You run on ahead, Kevin, and sound the fire bell.

We're going to move away at a steady pace. Karen, keep hold of my hand.

It's all right, Miss Chris. Sam is my eyes.

Jenny's gone all stiff!

Shock. This has brought back bad memories. Six months ago, when her home caught fire, Jenny was the only survivor. She lost all her family.

She's fainted!

I'll carry her. Let's get moving.

I hope this doesn't start Jenny having nightmares again. The matron at the Home told me she used to have very bad ones.

Kevin's ringing of the fire bell had alerted Dame Isobel.

Chris has got them all out, thank goodness! But it looks as though one of the children has been hurt.

101

Long Cool Drinks

Summer is for long, cool drinks. Here are a few from the Gale's Honey Bureau. Each recipe makes enough for one long drink, so you simply multiply the quantities by the number of people you are serving. (Use either imperial or metric measurements — do not mix.)

Always ask an adult before using any cooking equipment.

SPARKLING ORANGE AND BLACKCURRANT

75 ml. (3 fl. oz.) fresh orange juice
25 ml. (1 fl. oz.) blackcurrant puree
100 ml. (4 fl. oz.) lemonade
1 dessertspoon Gale's Clear Honey
Orange slices
Cucumber slices

Mix orange juice, blackcurrant puree and lemonade together. Stir in honey. Add ice, if required, then decorate with orange and cucumber slices.

STRAWBERRY YOGURT SHAKE

250 g. (9 oz.) natural yogurt
225 g. (8 oz.) strawberries, washed and hulled
3 tsps. Gale's Clear Honey
A few whole strawberries for decoration
Leaves for decoration (mint, bay, etc.)

Put yogurt, strawberries and honey in a blender to liquidise. When the mixture is frothy, pour into a large glass and decorate with strawberries and leaves.

ICED HONEY TEA

1 tsp. Gale's Clear Honey
275 ml. (½ pt.) cold tea
Slice lemon
Sprig mint

Stir honey into tea until dissolved. Chill. When ready to serve, garnish with lemon and mint.

Wishing Your Life Away

SANDY HARRIS was always wishing it were tomorrow, or the holidays, or her birthday. Everyone accused her of wishing her life away, but she took no notice. Until, in a junk shop . . .

That's an unusual looking clock. It's just what Mum would like for her birthday.

I'll take it — but why are you offering five pounds for its return?

Well, I've often sold it before — but, for some reason, people always come and sell it back to me.

£10
£5 refund on return

1988
JUN 15
WEDNESDAY

Sandy took her bargain home to wrap it up.

Its fantastic for ten pounds — got the date, day, and everything. Oh, it seems to be five minutes slow. I'll move it on.

Sandy moved the hands on five minutes, and —

That's odd — the country bus was here a second ago, and it disappeared the moment I altered the clock. I wonder . . . Dad arrives home at a quarter past five. So . . .

Sandy moved the hands forward again, and —

Hi, Sandy!

Er — Hi, Dad!

It can't be possible, can it — that if I advance the hands of the clock, time moves forward?

107

So, later—

Have a good weekend, Sandy.

See you Monday.

Great! Now I have two whole days to sort out this little problem at home.

1988 JUN 17 FRIDAY

But, at home —

So there's been no news of your missing daughter yet?

Not a word. She left home for school as usual yesterday. No-one saw her until lunch-time, then no-one saw her after lunch. The police are combing the area.

Of course! I never thought of that! I'd better do something about this — and quickly, too!

Sandy ran and hid in the garden shed.

Got to wind back the clock! If it can go forward, it can go back! But it's so slow — and they'll be here any second! Ah — Dad's drill has a screwdriver attachment that I could use to speed up the change.

Sandy attached the drill to the centre of the clock's hands, and wound frantically, but—

It must work! It must! I'll take it back to that junk shop and . . . and . . . I feel . . . Uuuuuuuh . . . .

When Sandy regained consciousness, it was cold.

Wh . . . what happened? I must have fainted! Oh! What's happened to the garden? It's not summer any more . . . and the house . . .

108

As you clean the saddle, look for frayed or broken stitching, especially where the girth straps join the body, or seat, of the saddle. Press on the front arch. If there is movement, or a noise, the tree is broken or damaged and the saddle should not be used on the pony until repaired. If, when pulled at either corner, the cantle or back end of the saddle bends, it has broken inside the padding, and, if the tree has also gone, it might be better to buy another saddle, since these would be major repairs. The damage is usually caused by dropping the saddle, letting it fall off a gate, or the pony rolling when saddled.

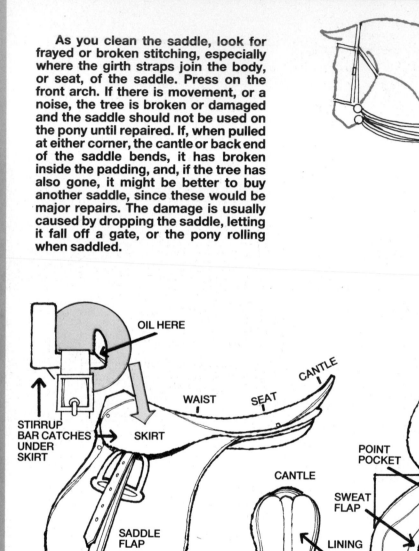

OIL HERE

CANTLE

WAIST   SEAT

STIRRUP
BAR CATCHES
UNDER
SKIRT   SKIRT

SADDLE
FLAP

CANTLE

SADDLE
FLAP

POINT
POCKET

SWEAT
FLAP

LINING

PANEL

GULLET

PANEL

BUCKLE
GUARD

GIRTH STRAPS

GIRTH STRAP

Oil the stirrup-bar catches. These should be left open when riding, to let the stirrup leather fall free if you topple off the pony. For it not to fall free could mean a nasty accident, with the fallen rider being dragged. Check girths — nylon ones for signs of splitting or getting tangled up; webbing ones for fraying; leather ones for suppleness and stitching at both ends. Check stirrup leathers for cracks near buckles, frayed or broken stitching, splits near the holes.

TACK

Tack should be both cleaned and checked regularly — preferably after each day's use, but, at the very least, once a week. Well-made tack can usually be repaired. It is advisable always to buy a well-known brand name, with good leather, rather than risk using imported tack.

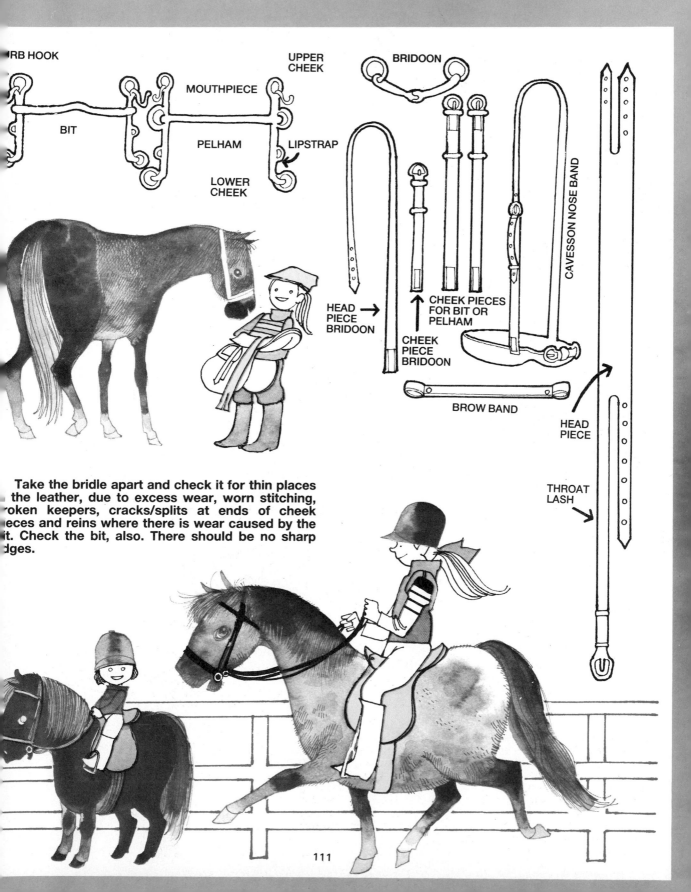

CURB HOOK

UPPER CHEEK

BRIDOON

MOUTHPIECE

BIT

PELHAM

LIPSTRAP

LOWER CHEEK

HEAD PIECE BRIDOON

CHEEK PIECE BRIDOON

CHEEK PIECES FOR BIT OR PELHAM

BROW BAND

CAVESSON NOSE BAND

HEAD PIECE

THROAT LASH

Take the bridle apart and check it for thin places the leather, due to excess wear, worn stitching, roken keepers, cracks/splits at ends of cheek eces and reins where there is wear caused by the t. Check the bit, also. There should be no sharp dges.

111

SPOT A PONY!

IT'S QUITE A **GAME**... SORTING OUT THESE CRAZY MIXED-UP PONIES!

CUT OUT THE DISC BELOW AND SEPARATE ALONG THE LINES INTO THREE CIRCLES. (TRACE OFF IF YOU DO NOT WANT TO CUT YOUR JUDY ANNUAL).

PASTE THE RINGS ONTO THIN CARD AND CUT OUT, LEAVING THE CENTRE INTACT. MAKE A HOLE IN THE CENTRE OF EACH AND JOIN TOGETHER WITH A PAPER FASTENER, AS SHOWN.

PASTE THE FOUR PONY TOKENS TO CARD AND CUT OUT. EACH ONE OF THEM CORRESPONDS TO ONE OF THE FOUR PONIES ON THE DISCS.

ANY NUMBER CAN PLAY THE GAME, TAKING TURNS TO THROW THE DIE THEN MOVING ONE OF THE DISCS — CLOCKWISE ONLY — IN RELATION TO THE OTHERS.

IF YOU THROW A "ONE" ON THE DIE, YOU MAKE A QUARTER TURN OF ONE OF THE DISCS — I.E. MOVING IT CLOCKWISE UNTIL THE STRAIGHT LINE AND THE PONIES AGAIN COINCIDE.

THERE ARE FOUR DIFFERENT COLOURED PONIES. YOU MOVE THE DISCS, ATTEMPTING TO COMPLETE A PONY OF THE SAME COLOUR ON ALL THREE DISCS. WHEN SUCCESSFUL, YOU CLAIM THE CORRESPONDING TOKEN.

CONTINUE LIKE THIS UNTIL ALL THE PONIES ARE CLAIMED, THE ONE HAVING THE MOST BEING THE WINNER. AS THE GAME PROGRESSES, IT GETS HARDER TO SPOT HOW TO MOVE THE DISCS. AS WELL AS GETTING PONIES FOR YOURSELF, YOU WILL ALSO TRY TO PREVENT YOUR OPPONENTS FROM SUCCEEDING.
HAVE FUN!

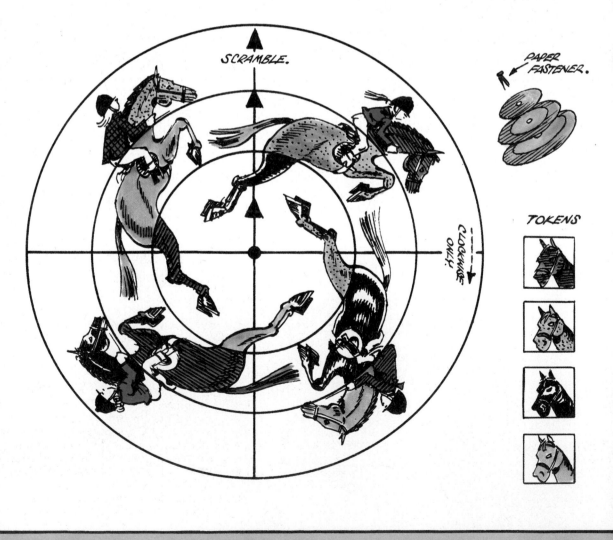

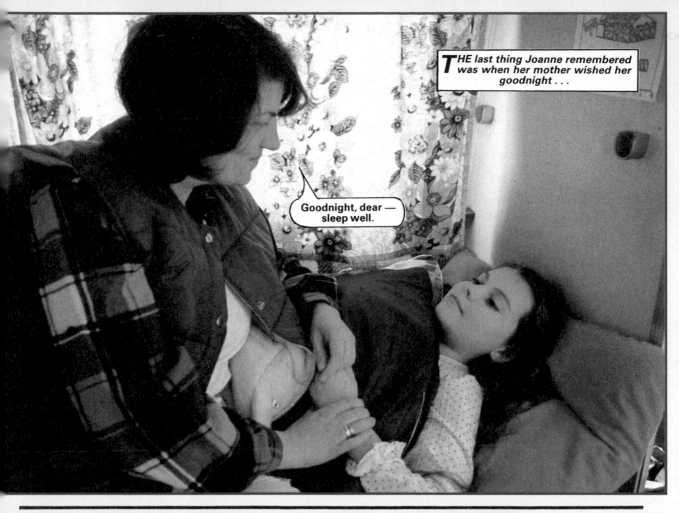

THE last thing Joanne remembered was when her mother wished her goodnight . . .

Goodnight, dear — sleep well.

INTERRUPTED HOLIDAY

Joanne Edwards was on a caravan holiday with her mum, her younger sister, Sara, and their dog, Oscar.

Early next morning —

Wake up, Joanne! Mum's not here! We're all alone in the caravan!

D-don't panic, Sara — she might have gone to do some shopping.

113

115

Quick Pizza

The favourite food of rich and poor alike, the pizza originated in Naples and has now become as popular worldwide as it has always been in Italy. Cheap and easy to make, the pizza is served cut into small squares with drinks, as a quick snack, or as a substantial meal.

First make the tomato topping. Put all the ingredients — including the juice from the tin of tomatoes — into a pan. Season with salt and pepper. Gently cook for 30 minutes without a lid, reducing the mixture to a thick pulp. Check for seasoning.

While the tomato mixture is cooking, make the scone base. Sift flour, baking powder and salt into a large bowl. Rub in the butter and mix to a soft dough with milk. Turn onto a large, floured baking sheet, then roll to a 10 inch (254 mm.) circle for the pizza base. Spread the two tablespoons of Colman's French mustard evenly over the base.

When the tomato mixture is cooked, spread over the dough to within one inch (25 mm.) of the edge. Now you can choose one of the following toppings:—

1. 4 oz. (100 g.) sliced salami
2. 4 oz. (100 g.) mixed peppers, peas and sweetcorn
3. 2 oz. (50 g.) sliced mushrooms plus 2 oz. (50 g.) diced ham
4. 4 oz. (100 g.) sardines

Once you have added your chosen topping, sprinkle with 6 oz. (175 g.) strong cheddar cheese plus one tablespoon grated parmesan.

Bake at 400° F. (200° C., Gas Mark 6) for about 30-40 minutes until well risen and brown round the edges.

TOMATO TOPPING

- 1 lb. 12 oz. (800 g.) can of tomatoes
- 1 medium Spanish onion, chopped
- 2 tablespoons tomato puree
- 2 teaspoons dried oregano
- 1 level teaspoon sugar
- Salt and ground black pepper

SCONE PIZZA BASE

- 8 oz. (225 g.) self-raising flour
- 1 level teaspoon baking powder
- 1 level teaspoon salt
- 1 oz. (25 g.) butter, softened about ¼ pint (150 ml.) milk
- 2 tablespoons Colman's French Mustard

Always ask an adult before using any cooking appliance.

118

Long Distance

Ah! I thought I remembered seeing it up here among Great-Grandmother's junk! Just the thing for the school play!

A S soon as she saw the old telephone, Jean Marshall knew it was just what she was looking for.

So you found the old 'phone, Jean. Your great-grandmother was one of the first people in the district to have a telephone installed.

Our play takes place in the early 1900's, Mum. This 'phone will look great on the set.

Next day, in the school hall—

It looks good, Jean. I'll wire it up so that it will ring when the script calls for it.

Thanks, Brian. And then I answer it as Lady Meredith.

Later—

The old 'phone's ringing. I suppose I'd better answer it, then. It might be a message for Lady Meredith.

Hello, my dear. Isn't it exciting that the French aviator, Monsieur Bleriot, has actually flown over the English Channel? How convenient to be on the telephone, especially now that I'm confined to bed.

Hello! Hello! Who is this, please?

119

120

122

123

I went into a toyshop
　　To buy myself a ball,
But ended up with something
　　That I didn't want at all.
For, on the shelf above me,
　　Staring down with piercing eye,
A bright red furry crocodile
　　Dared me to pass him by.

At first I just ignored him,
　　But that didn't work at all.
I tried to leave the shop and go
　　Elsewhere to get a ball.
His eyes were boring in my back,
　　So I turned around to see
What made him so determined
　　He would leave the shop with *me.*

He wasn't even lifelike—
　　His shoulders were too square—
And who'd expect a crocodile
　　To have red, fuzzy hair?
I knew that we'd have battles if
　　I bought him. But it's funny
How I felt that I *must* have him,
　　Though he cost a lot of money.

The Boss

I took him home and wondered . . .
        Should I really let him in,
With all those rick-rack teeth on show
        In such a fiendish grin?
He didn't waste a minute,
        And at once demanded food.
I offered him an apple,
        But that wasn't any good.

He stared all round the kitchen,
        Then pounced upon a chop.
He ate it raw, then seized a loaf—
        I thought he'd never stop.
I goggled in amazement
        At that ruthless crocodile.
I watched him drink a pint of milk,
        And then begin to smile.

But it's no good feeling sorry
        That I've bought that reptile red.
He's moved in now for years to come —
        Or is this a dream, instead?